RAIL
OPERATIONS

JOHN GLOVER

Ian Allan
PUBLISHING

Contents

First published 1999

ISBN 0 7110 2689 0

Published by Ian Allan Publishing

an imprint of Ian Allan Publishing Ltd, Terminal House, Shepperton, Surrey TW17 8AS.
Printed by Ian Allan Printing Ltd, Riverdene Business Park, Hersham, Surrey KT12 4RG.

Code: 9911/C

Front cover:
York in May 1998 with a Virgin CrossCountry service from Bristol Temple Meads to Newcastle. *Author*

Back cover:
HAA hopper wagons await attention at Knottingley in May 1998. *Author*

Title page:
The 15.05 Norwich to Liverpool Street arrives at Ipswich behind No 86221 *BBC Look East* on 13 April 1999. There are indications on the platform as to where passengers should stand to find the various coach letters. *Author*

Below:
The railings outside Marylebone station and the gates which guard the entrance bear plentiful memories of its builder, the Great Central Railway. *Author*

Right:
'Not all railway problems are this easy to solve!' The author hopes that this book will shed a little light on the operational side of the railway. *Author's collection, by kind permission of Carmen Systems of Sweden, transport scheduling specialists*

Bibliography

The dearth of recent literature in this subject is surprising. Despite their age, the following were found by the author to contain useful contributions on the subject:

Practical Railway Working, Charles Travis, David R. Lamb, John A. Jenkinson. The Boswell Printing & Publishing Co Ltd, 1915.
British Railway Operation, T. Bernard Hare, Modern Transport Publishing Co Ltd, 1930.
Practical Railway Operating, T. Bernard Hare, Modern Transport Publishing Co Ltd, undated, c1935.
Modern Railway Operation, David R. Lamb, Sir Isaac Pitman & Sons Ltd, Third Edition, 1941.
Requirements for Passenger Lines and Recommendations for Goods Lines of the Minister of Transport in Regard to Railway Construction and Operation, HMSO, 1950.
Modern Railways, Brian Reed, Temple Press Ltd, 1950.
Railway Operating Practice, H. Samuel, Odhams Press Ltd, 1961.

Of more recent publications, perhaps the following principal sources should be mentioned:

The Law of the Railway, Leslie James, Barry Rose (Publishers) Ltd, 1980.
British Railways Track: Design, Construction and Maintenance, Ed G. H. Cope, Permanent Way Institution, Sixth Edition 1993.
Rail Transport Management, Chartered Institute of Transport, September 1993.
Railway Safety Principles and Guidance, Part 1 and Part 2, Sections A to F, HSE Books, all 1996.
Network Management Statement, Railtrack PLC, 1999.
Modern Railways magazine, various issues, Ian Allan Publishing Ltd.

Not all railway problems are this easy to solve!

Acknowledgements

My greatest debt is to Peter Ashton, formerly of West Anglia & Great Northern Railway, whose direct and extensive knowledge of matters operational has been of great assistance, being much more recent than the author's. As always, my thanks go to Derek Mercer for his hard work in printing my negatives.

Introduction

The main line railways of Britain date almost in their entirety from the Victorian era; the last to reach London in the form of the Great Central was installed at Marylebone in 1899. They were business enterprises, conceived in the days long before the internal combustion engine, when water transport and the horse, with a cart for goods, were the principal competitors.

Many have lyricised over the engineering triumphs of the Stephensons and the Brunels and, later, the locomotive engineers such as Collett, Bulleid, Stanier and Gresley. Triumphs they indeed were, but their creations needed a context within which to work. How was the railway to be organised so that the system could give of its best? This requires a concentration on the more mundane but nevertheless crucial fields, such as line capacity, station design, operational planning and the handling of goods.

The principal objective of this book is to set out in a concise form the various operational matters which help to make the modern railway work, or not, as the case may be. At the very least, it is hoped that it will give cause for thought. Some might argue that new brooms in the railway industry were overdue, but the mechanics of making the system work to the best advantage of the industry and its customers deserve more attention than they have had of late.

Perhaps the principal conclusion to be drawn is that the results achieved are those of a partnership between the infrastructure company, the passenger and freight operating companies, the rolling stock manufacturers and leasing companies, and all the other bodies who contribute in one way or another. The industry may now be fragmented, but the mechanics of getting the best out of the railway have changed little.

There is certainly a place for the adversarial role, but the same forces are at play. Thus, competition between the West Coast and the East Coast main lines reached a climax in 1895. The results of the 'Race to the North' depended upon slickness in matters such as engine changes, obtaining priorities over other traffic where needed and ensuring staff and equipment were in top form. It was operational matters such as these that decided which company's train would be the first to reach Kinnaber Junction, where the lines converged for the final few miles into Aberdeen.

The author trusts that *abc Railway Operations* will prove a helpful contribution to those directly involved in operational matters, as well as those with a general interest in the topic.

John Glover
Worcester Park
October 1999

The 1993 Act

The days of the unified railway, exemplified by the British Railways Board, are now over. In 1992, the Conservative government published a White Paper. Subtitled 'The Privatisation of British Rail', it was published on 14 July. On objectives it had little to say, referring only to a wish 'to improve the quality of rail services'.

The resulting Railways Act 1993 brought about a fundamental reorganisation of the way in which operations on Britain's railway system are conducted. This was a substantial piece of legislation, which ran to an Act of 154 Sections and 14 Schedules. The change in the structure of the industry was based upon the separation of the management of the railway infrastructure from the operation of the trains which run upon it. For passenger operations, there was the further separation of the ownership of rolling stock. On this was imposed obligations on passenger service provision through a Director of Franchising, usually in return for some public funding, with a separate regulatory body to protect the interests of users and to promote the use of the railway.

1.

Railway Organisation

The Act's main provisions came into effect on 1 April 1994, and the franchising of the 25 passenger Train Operating Companies was completed on 31 March 1997. The sale of the last nationalised operating company of the British Railways Board was that of Railfreight Distribution (RfD), which passed into the private sector on 22 November 1997.

Railway Infrastructure

Since 1 April 1994, the ownership and operation of the infrastructure of track, signalling, stations and other structures has been vested in Railtrack, itself now a private sector company.

Railtrack PLC is responsible for granting train operators access rights to the track, and charging them for that access. The company is responsible for central timetabling, train

Left:
A hotel was built opposite Marylebone station, linked by a covered walkway. The station is seen on the right in this view of 17 December 1998, very nearly a century after the whole was built. For many years what was and now once again is the hotel, was the headquarters offices of the British Transport Commission and then the British Railways Board. *Author*

Right:
Co-ordination still reigns at Liverpool Street; this joint National Railways and London Transport declaration may be seen on the east, Bishopsgate, side. The date is 13 April 1999. *Author*

planning and signalling. Railtrack has a network licence authorising it to be the operator of the network.

The company's main business activities include:

- selling train paths to train operators, managing the allocation of train paths, and producing the working timetable;
- operating the rail network, including signalling, and supplying electricity for traction to train operators;
- operating the 14 major stations;
- leasing stations and light maintenance depots to Train Operating Companies;
- maintaining and renewing the railway infrastructure;
- planning and executing major capital programmes; and
- managing its property portfolio.

The maintenance of the railway network is a Railtrack responsibility, the work being contracted out to infrastructure maintenance companies.

Railtrack also has an important role in managing safety on the network, though there may be changes here. In addition to being responsible for the safety of its infrastructure, including the control of its contractors and of the trains on its network, Railtrack oversees safety matters affecting the use of its network by train and station operators. It is responsible for the formulation of mandatory network-wide safety standards and monitors the safety performance of train and station operators having access to its network.

Railtrack derives nearly 90% of its revenue from access charges to the passenger franchisees. The company receives no direct subsidy from the government, but obtains some grants in respect of investment in its infrastructure. Railtrack is, however, indirectly dependent on public financial support since its principal customers, the Train Operating Companies (TOCs), receive significant amounts of public financial support by way of subsidy or grant. The subsidy element is declining over time, in line with the contracts signed by the TOCs with the Franchising Director. It is presently an open question as to what might happen when the franchises come up for renewal. Franchise extension in return for specified additional consumer benefits may be a possibility. Apart from the Island Line on the Isle of Wight (October 2001), the first franchises expire early in 2003.

One of Railtrack's duties under its Network Licence is the annual publication of a Network Management Statement (NMS). The purpose of the NMS is to achieve a shared understanding of Railtrack's plans for the management and enhancement of the network for the ensuing decade, with more detail for the earlier years of the programme. To do this, Railtrack has to take views on the likely future growth rates of rail traffic, both passenger and freight, and make proposals as to how this can be accommodated on the system.

Train Operating Companies

The main passenger operations are in the hands of 25 Train Operating Companies, which equate broadly with the former operating businesses of the British Railways Board. All now have franchise agreements with the Director of Passenger Rail Franchising. For the services in their areas which they support, the Passenger Transport Executives are co-signatories.

To fulfil its franchise obligations, a TOC needs:

• to have guaranteed rights of access to track and other infrastructure, and use of the relevant stations;
• to receive passenger revenues, and have access to common services such as tele-communications and information systems;
• to own or have use of the necessary operational assets — mainly rolling stock and maintenance facilities; and
• to employ the operational and revenue staff.

Franchising Director

It was the duty of the Franchising Director to receive competitive bids for a level of public funding to run a rail service for a period of time. Each successful bidder for a franchise was given the rights and obligations to operate certain passenger rail services. The franchises are generally of seven years, but if the agreement involves substantial replacement of rolling stock, then the term has, in some cases, been extended up to 15 years. The franchise documents also specify the quality of service to be provided.

The service levels themselves were specified to a greater or lesser extent under a Passenger Service Requirement (PSR). The Franchising Director's role is to secure the provision of improved railway passenger services through the franchise agreements. He is responsible for paying public subsidy to franchisees where necessary.

Franchise agreements are structured so that franchisees have to meet defined performance standards. These are contractual obligations for an operator and specify, where necessary: minimum service levels, frequency, and quality of service (punctuality and reliability). In some cases, the Franchising Director sets limits on the degree to which a franchisee may raise certain fares. Service standards are monitored by the Franchising Director throughout the life of the franchise.

In most cases, there is a formal incentive for franchisees to perform above the minimum standards set. This incentive is shared with Railtrack. Where an operator fails to meet minimum agreed standards, there may be penalties.

In letting the franchises, the Office of Passenger Rail Franchising (OPRAF) needed to ensure:

• service and value for the passenger;
• value for money for the taxpayer;
• success and profit for the franchisees; and
• long-term development of the railway.

The TOCs, formerly part of British Rail, became private sector companies at the commencement of their franchises.

Licences

Each TOC has a licence to operate trains. TOCs obtain the use of track by means of an access agreement with Railtrack. They also enter into agreements with Railtrack for access to the major stations and lease from Railtrack other stations and the light maintenance depots which they operate. Access to the stations and light maintenance depots operated by a particular TOC may then be obtained by other TOCs under access agreements with the first TOC. Station and depot operation each require separate licences.

Rolling Stock Companies

Initially three private-sector rolling stock leasing companies (ROSCOs) owned all the rolling stock which might be required for passenger services. This stock, consisting of electric and diesel multiple-units, coaching stock and locomotives, is then leased to the Train Operating Companies. Typically, these leases are coterminous with the franchise period. The companies are Angel Trains Contracts, Forward Trust Rail and

Porterbrook Leasing, and each started by owning what was considered to be a balanced portfolio.

The ROSCOs are responsible for renewing their portfolios of rolling stock as and when they think fit. They do not have in-house maintenance facilities. Specified light maintenance is the responsibility of the TOCs, but heavy maintenance and refurbishment is contracted out by the ROSCOs. Subsequently, deals between the TOCs, ROSCOs and manufacturers have been concluded for new vehicles, and a few are owned outright by TOCs.

Freight Companies

The arrangements for freight traffic are broadly similar. Initially, English, Welsh & Scottish Railway and Freightliner owned their locomotive fleets themselves, and much of the rolling stock. Subsequently, some Freightliner locomotives have been transferred to Porterbrook Leasing and hired back by the operating company, and the new builds for EWS are owned by Angel Trains Contracts. Many wagons are the property of the companies whose goods they carry by rail, as has long been the case. OPRAF is not involved in freight operations.

A contractual matrix links the respective responsibilities of these organisations and also those of the many others involved. Naturally, these contracts include provision for payments between the organisations for services rendered.

Rail Regulator

An important appointment is that of the Rail Regulator, whose statutory duties are set out in the Railways Act. He has a specific duty to protect the interests of rail users, including passengers, operators, and other customers of the system. The Regulator takes a close interest in access charges in relation to the quality of service provided by Railtrack.

The Regulator is also required to promote the use and development of the railway network, to foster efficiency and competition, and to facilitate through-ticketing and other benefits of a national network. He is also obliged to avoid over-regulation, so that railway operators, Railtrack and the Franchising Director can carry out their business without undue hindrance.

The Regulator considers applications for licences, approves access agreements and protects consumer interests through his sponsorship of consumer committees. He also decides whether proposals to close passenger services, networks and facilities should be allowed, after he has received reports from consumer committees and subject to appeal to the Secretary of State.

All railway operators, including those operating stations, must have a licence to ensure that they are fit to operate (or else a formal exemption). The issue of a licence will depend on the operator having a satisfactory safety case accepted by Railtrack.

The licences contain specific obligations and also general obligations such as to have adequate insurance cover and to produce an environmental policy. Most include a requirement for the licensee to use the services of the British Transport Police.

Access agreements are subject to the approval of the Regulator, who can also direct owners of relevant facilities to grant access agreements to operators. Once the Regulator has approved an access agreement, changes to it can be made only with his consent.

Railway Inspectorate

There are also a number of supporting bodies. Her Majesty's Railway Inspectorate (HMRI) is part of the Health & Safety Executive. The Railway Inspectorate's objectives are to ensure the continued safety of Britain's railways by the following means:

- The issue of guidance for railway operators on the design, construction and operation of railways.
- Prior inspection and approval of new lines, rolling stock and equipment.
- The monitoring of safety procedures on existing lines, to ensure compliance with the Health and Safety at Work Act and relevant statutory provisions.
- The investigation of selected accidents, and the study of accident trends to identify priorities for improvement.

Below:
Waterloo International station is grafted on to the former Windsor side at Waterloo. This is a relatively unfamiliar view of the terminal building, taken on 1 September 1998; that it is a station is not immediately apparent. *Author*

All operators have to submit a Railway Safety Case (RSC). This demonstrates that an operator has the systems in place to manage operations safely and meets required safety standards. It includes a safety policy, a risk assessment, a description of safety management systems, and the safety side of maintenance and operational arrangements.

The RSCs of train and station operators must be validated and accepted by Railtrack, which also regularly monitors them. Railtrack's own RSC must be validated and accepted by HMRI, who also view other operators' safety cases to ensure that they are properly considered by Railtrack. HMRI is also concerned with the standards of competence for safety-critical staff, and is responsible for enforcement.

HMRI publishes a comprehensive set of documents giving guidance on Railway Safety Principles.

British Transport Police

The British Transport Police is a specialised and dedicated police service to the railway industry. It is responsible for maintaining law and order throughout the railways and has similar powers and responsibilities to other Police Forces. All licensed operators, for example Railtrack and passenger and freight operators, are required to enter into Police Service Agreements (PSAs) for core police service provision. This is a licence condition. Other operators who are exempt, for example Midland Metro, may also enter into PSAs if they so wish.

Strategic Rail Authority

The 1998 White Paper presaged the establishment of a Strategic Rail Authority (SRA), which will be a statutory body with board members appointed by ministers. The SRA will provide a focus for strategic planning of the passenger and freight railways with appropriate powers to influence the behaviour of key industry players. Specifically, the duties of the authority will include:

- promotion of the use of the railway within an integrated transport system;
- ensuring that the railways are operated as a coherent network;
- ensuring that rail transport options constitute good value for money;
- taking a view on the capacity of the railway, assessing investment needs and identifying priorities; and
- drawing up policies and criteria for future passenger rail competition.

The SRA will support integrated transport initiatives and provide for the first time a clear focus for the promotion of rail freight. It will also encompass the present duties of OPRAF, and it will become the main regulator of passenger benefits. Enforcement procedures will be tightened up, and Section 55 of the 1993 Act amended.

However, this is yet to become law. While a shadow SRA has been established, its new powers will have to await the enactment of a Transport Bill.

The above is intended as a concise introduction to the arrangements under which today's railway operations take place. The principles of safe, reliable and effective operation have changed little, but some understanding of the present organisational and the essentially contractual background is perhaps essential.

Left:
The pantograph on a train has a wide range of heights at which it can operate, to take account of the clearances required at level crossings on the one hand and under bridgework on the other. In this view, at Longbridge on 22 October 1997 on a Class 323 unit, it is virtually at its lowest.
Author

2.

Principles of Operation

'In principle, the prospects of any electrification are simple. The operating economies which you derive from cheaper traction, cheaper maintenance, greater utilisation of rolling stock are just about offset by the increased cost of a more frequent service. Therefore, the interest on and the amortisation of the capital must come from increased revenue.' G. F. Fiennes, I Tried to Run a Railway. Ian Allan Ltd, 1967.

Thus, Gerry Fiennes, General Manager of the Eastern Region of British Railways, described the justification for the widespread suburban electrification of the Great Eastern and London, Tilbury & Southend services. This work was completed at the beginning of the 1960s. As so often happens with generalisations, though, there are important elements omitted. In this case, it concerns the revenue. There is an implicit assumption that the revenue potential is there. In other words, that if electrification proceeds, the catchment area of the new services plus their own excellence in terms of quality and frequency, and the marketing efforts, can produce enough traffic to recoup the capital costs.

In reality, that electrification scheme omitted the Lea Valley through Tottenham Hale and on to Cheshunt, plus the sundry branches such as Romford-Upminster. Examination of the geography of the Lea Valley will show why. Certainly at the southern end and close to the River Lea Navigation, the area is mainly industrial and contains little housing. The latter is situated on the higher ground to the west and nearer the Enfield Town line, itself less than a mile distant throughout. That the Lea Valley was

electrified in 1969 owed more to the opening of the Victoria Line of London Underground to Tottenham Hale in 1968, and the operational inconvenience of having a non-electrified line which could be a useful diversionary route, in the middle of otherwise electrified territory. Local traffic was, and remains, modest.

With this mildly cautionary tale in mind, the reader is invited to consider the following principles affecting railway operations:

1. The service which railway companies provide and for which they are paid is movement.

The customer, whether as a passenger or a freight forwarder, wants to see the task for which he has paid performed within what he considers to be a reasonable length of time, with due regard to safety and quality of service issues. Time spent stationary does not earn revenue for the operator. It also incurs costs, to the extent that the carrier remains responsible for the safety and security of the passenger or goods throughout the journey.

Right:
At Kenton, a DVT on an up Virgin service overtakes a 1972 stock train of London Underground on the Bakerloo Line. This section of track is all owned by Railtrack, for which LUL pays access charges. The date is 27 October 1998. *Author*

2. Faster journey times allow the same rolling stock and staff to provide a more frequent service.

If the time taken for a journey can be reduced from (say) 5hr to 4hr, this creates a spare hour in which the train and train crew can be utilised elsewhere. Cumulatively, with the benefits spread across the service as a whole, this can result in service frequencies being increased with a less than proportionate increase in rolling stock requirements. Alternatively, of course, the same service levels can be provided with fewer vehicles.

3. Load factors are all-important.

Revenue is earned by the carriage of people and goods, and not by moving empty vehicles around. Railways are unusual among the transport modes in that there is no general limitation as to the volumes of passengers which can be carried on one train. This allows passengers to cram themselves on; while this may be acceptable for short-distance operations, it is much less so for longer distance services. Conversely, the conveyance of empty seats represents an immediate waste of resources; they cannot be stored for sale subsequently. A top priority must be to make the maximum use of the capacity provided, but not to the extent

that serious overcrowding becomes a problem. Similarly, a wagon which is less than fully loaded will cost the operator virtually the same amount to move as a full one, though there will be some limitations on total train weights or lengths.

4. Peak demand is difficult to cater for economically.

The peak requirement is associated most readily with the Monday to Friday morning and afternoon peaks on suburban passenger services, during which the demand for carriage is several times that experienced at other times. However, many other peaks may be experienced throughout the railway passenger industry. These include, for instance, seasonal and holiday peaks, different volumes on different days of the week, or in conjunction with special events of any nature. A further variation in the type of accommodation required, particularly the proportions of First and Standard Class.

Catering for a peak flow inevitably requires more capital equipment in the form of trains, for which the usage outside the peak period may be low. To some extent, it may be possible to redeploy equipment; summer weekend holiday train services traditionally use trains which are required

primarily for business travel during the week. Thus the Summer Saturdays only 06.58 Birmingham New Street to Ramsgate and the 12.10 return working (to Glasgow Central!) is formed from an ordinary Virgin CrossCountry set.

However, the daily suburban peak is the most difficult. Not only trains, but also the infrastructure which supports them and the staffing levels have to be geared to a situation where the only worthwhile revenue-earning usage may be as low as one journey into town in the morning and one out in the evening. Such trains may be made up to a maximum of 12 cars depending on the route restrictions of the line concerned. These cars also have to be maintained and stabled.

Peaks occur also in the freight businesses, for seasonal reasons, but also because customer requirements for overnight transits concentrate operations into a portion of the day. Nowhere is this more apparent than in the Royal Mail traffic, which will be considered later.

5. Rail traffics are interdependent.

The railway is effectively a closed system, on which at any one time a variety of traffics will be running. These will be the trains of different companies, fast and stopping,

passenger and freight. It may be assumed that a balance has been struck to the extent that if everything proceeds according to plan and to timetable, all will work as intended.

However, the system must be robust enough to cope with change. On a day-to-day basis, there will always be some instances of equipment failure, staff not turning up on time, holding trains for late-running connections, and so on. All will have their effects on performance, but it is at best difficult to isolate the effects entirely. Thus, junction conflicts take place where at least one of the trains concerned will be delayed, and holding a connection occupies a platform which may be required for a subsequent train. The system of operation must be resilient, in the sense that there is sufficient (but not too much) slack time to allow recovery. Staff will respond to challenges, which will keep them on their toes provided there is a reasonable chance of success. Too generous timings, on the contrary, tend to lead to sloppiness.

Where future planning is concerned, matters become more difficult. The railway must not be allowed to ossify, but a tightly run timetable may have few spare train paths. Or there may be a way of accommodating a new service, but this

Above:
A Thameslink service with No 319368 approaches Sutton from the 'Wall of Death' on the Wimbledon loop on 12 February 1999. The train has just restarted from the signal protecting the junction on the 1 in 44 gradient up into the station. On the left of the picture, the four-aspect signal shows a single yellow, indicating that the line is clear to the next signal on the main line towards Epsom. If the route was set for Wimbledon, the 'feather' at the top of the signal would also be illuminated. *Author*

requires a bit of flexibility in some of those presently provided.

One of the results of Virgin Trains' proposed 15min service from Euston to Birmingham on the West Coast main line (WCML) would be that the local services from Coventry to Birmingham New Street are likely to have to spend 7min waiting to be overtaken at Birmingham International.

This is a two-track railway, and Birmingham International's five platforms are the only opportunities available for overtaking. Could some traffics be diverted elsewhere, and what are the practicalities and costs of laying some additional running lines on the existing route?

The other alternative is to run local services fast from Coventry to International and then all stations to New Street, with the next service all stations Coventry to International and fast to New Street. But this increases train miles, if the same level of services is to be provided to the local stations. At the very least, it forces a rethink on the local service run by Central Trains, who operate it on behalf of Centro, the Passenger Transport Executive.

The message here is that train planning decisions cannot be taken in isolation; contractual conditions there may be in some flows, but some give and take is needed to run the railway efficiently. There will always be winners and losers, but this is a continuous process and all parties stand to benefit sometimes as well as lose at other times.

6. Line capacity is a scarce resource.

From the infrastructure owner's point of view, trains are judged on the extent to which they occupy the railway. The railway is divided into signal sections, each of which may be occupied by only one train at any given time. In multiple-aspect signalling areas, these sections will be of broadly similar areas.

A slow or stopping train takes longer to travel through a section than a fast train. Thus, a slow train also uses up more line capacity than a fast one. The worst situation is when fast and slow trains alternate, as will be discussed in detail later.

If increasing levels of traffic are both expected and to be encouraged, then the best use must be made of the infrastructure that exists. Further work may of course be considered and Railtrack's Network Management Statement identifies many such schemes to relieve problem areas. However, such work is costly and can only be undertaken over a considerable period of time, even when funding is agreed.

Is the best use being made of each train path? Where capacity is virtually fully subscribed, running a single-car diesel unit on a local service makes little sense if this denies track access to a 1,000-tonne freight or a 10-car passenger train. Where does the balance of benefits and costs lie? It is in areas such as this that hard decisions may have to be taken in future. The structure of charges made by the infrastructure owner and how they may be varied between traffics will also bear heavily on the outcome. Such matters, however, are beyond the scope of this volume.

7. Short turnrounds are a key to utilisation.

In the days of steam traction, it was necessary for main line locomotives to be detached from the incoming passenger train at the terminus, and then to run round the coaching stock and reattach. Some servicing would probably be required and, if a tender locomotive, it would normally need to visit a turntable. The alternative was to have another locomotive to take the train out, thus releasing the incoming train locomotive. The train might leave the terminus as empty stock to the sidings for servicing, or as an outgoing passenger service.

Such movements continued into the diesel and electric era. However, the advent of multiple-unit diesel and electric rolling stock for local services was a huge benefit. By comparison, all the driver has to do is to walk to the driving cab at the other end of his train; even with a brake test, the time spent stationary need not exceed 5min. Neither the run-round facilities, use of which usually requires the adjacent platform to be empty, nor a second locomotive, are needed. Terminals can be that much smaller as a result, but the real gain is in rolling stock utilisation.

In the past two decades, the construction of Driving Van Trailers or similar has enabled even main line express services to adopt the multiple-unit method of working. The result is simpler station terminal layouts with the total number of movements much reduced, and the ability to reverse trains much more quickly. The main limitations are related to service reliability, in the sense that a scheduled 5min turnround is unhelpful if the train is frequently 10min late, and the time necessary for any train preparation required before taking up its next journey.

On the freight side, similar considerations led to the introduction of the colliery to power station merry-go-round services.

8. Good performance is vital.

Trains should not, however, be late. On the passenger railway, standards are prescribed within the terms of OPRAF's passenger franchises. They are enforced with the aid of penalties, while better performance can be rewarded.

The standards refer to reliability in the sense of whether a train runs at all, and punctuality. A punctual train is one which arrives at its destination either on time or within a certain period. This is normally within 5min for short distance services and 10min for others.

The performance of the railway industry has been patchy, but generally declining on both measures in 1998/9; this has brought down predictable governmental wrath. But service performance is important for the operator too. If the services are tightly timed with good stock and staff utilisation, lateness will have knock-on effects into subsequent services. Matters can easily snowball, to the extent that widespread cancellations become necessary to restore order. The only alternative is the costly injection of additional resources of vehicles and men, neither of which may be available anyway. Overall, customers are dissatisfied and operating expenses rise.

9. Surplus facilities may be an embarrassment.

There has been a noticeable trend in recent years to shed rolling stock; what used to take X units to run a service now takes X minus one third. Similarly, a terminal which once supported 16 platforms now only supports 11, or what used to be a four-track section of line is now reduced to three or even two tracks.

Facilities cost money, and if they are not *really* needed they are a drain on company resources. They are also likely to lead to inefficiency. Operators and engineers alike will fight for more rather than less, as it does make their respective jobs easier. More units takes the pressure off tight turnround times

for the operator, while extra tracks give the permanent way engineer more alternatives when planning his maintenance work. But it also builds in a higher cost base. From Railtrack's point of view, spare line capacity enables the company to accept additional bids for its use, but this is of no value if operators do not wish to use it. From this standpoint, anyway, excess should be avoided.

On the other hand, some spare capacity allows flexibility in what is offered. More rolling stock than is required to run the basic service allows a TOC to strengthen train formations, run charters, deploy some elsewhere, or perhaps earn a few pounds by subleasing to others. Railtrack's empty main line can allow the incumbent operator to run additional services; it could likewise allow one of his competitors to do exactly the same thing, subject to the competition rules. But from Railtrack's point of view, it is of little concern where the access charges come from, as long as they do indeed come.

Circumstances have changed with the demise of the corporate railway, and different considerations are relevant depending upon where in the hierarchy a company stands. However, it remains true from the railway industry point of view that truly spare capacity, be it in infrastructure, rolling stock or facilities, represents a cost to be avoided wherever possible.

10. The customer is the best judge of what he wants.

The most costly and technically excellent pieces of equipment have no value to the business, unless they are employed to earn revenue. Furthermore, the greater the use to which they are put, the more that they have the potential to earn. But what does the passenger or, with suitable amendments, the freight customer want? What is the trade-off between journey time, price, punctuality, comfort, seat width and pitch, service frequency, on-board train services, station services, ease of ticketing, guarantee of a seat, etc, etc? How does this differ for those travelling on business, to work or for education purposes, visiting friends and relations, shopping and leisure activities? What is the value put on being able to travel on a through service? Are there variations between time of day, day of week, season of the year, for different age groups, or between men and women? Do British nationals have different ideas from the visiting businessmen and tourists from overseas?

The operator may plan an economical and well-thought-out service, but it needs to match the aspirations of the customers. Market research is a valuable tool, which can be used to pinpoint business strengths and opportunities as well as weaknesses and threats. If there are no customers, there is no need for the railway.

11. The railway does not exist in a vacuum.

A weakness of the railway is that access to stations frequently requires another mode of transport to and from the real origins and destinations of trips. Only one third of all train journeys are direct in the sense that they do not require interchange, either to another mode of transport or to another train. (Walking is not counted.) Even local station access may be a bus, car or bicycle ride away, while a business destination in a town may require a taxi ride from the nearest station. Interchange is a necessary attribute of many journeys which use the railway in part, whether between main line and local rail services at major stations such as Leeds, or to and from local non-rail transport.

The acquisition of some rail franchises by bus-based groups has led to a welcome interest in the bus+rail services, often in conjunction with through-ticketing. This may result in additional services which can be thought of as rail connections and thus need to be considered in the timetable planning process, while the provision of bus stands, taxi ranks, cycle racks and car parks at stations might need to assume a higher priority.

12. Change takes time.

The operational railway has two main opportunities to change its timetables each year in May and October, for which the lead times are over a year. Investment schemes of any magnitude will take much longer to bring to fruition.

The starting place for a new project is to

Right
The Driving Open Brake Standards on the Norwich services are fully fledged passenger vehicles, formerly operating in Scotland. They are of the Mk2f variety. The 08.30 Liverpool Street to Norwich passes No 315804 at Stratford on 8 February 1990, the latter proceeding to depot. *Author*

define the concept. This then leads to the feasibility stage, at which the interested parties get together, identify the issues and agree a way forward. This is likely to include technical studies and economic/financial appraisal, from which it is hoped that a clear single option is identified. Success here heralds the detailed design and development work which has to be undertaken, together with matters such as obtaining statutory consents if these are needed. The funding also has to be finalised. This then allows the construction work to be undertaken.

With the best will in the world, change cannot be achieved instantaneously; a secondary item in the case of infrastructure work is the disruption to rail traffics which may be caused by the undertaking of the works themselves. Use of diversionary routes due to temporary line closures requires drivers with the necessary route knowledge, and possibly a change of traction. Journey times will be extended, which may mean the commitment of additional resources to cover. Some passengers may be put off from travelling. This is in no sense an argument against undertaking such work, merely that there are these less obvious costs to be considered as well and that the whole project has to be properly managed.

The suggested principles of railway operation are repeated below for ease of reference:

1. The service which railway companies provide and for which they are paid is movement.
2. Faster journey times allow the same rolling stock and staff to provide a more frequent service.
3. Load factors are all-important.
4. Peak demand is difficult to cater for economically.
5. Rail traffics are interdependent.
6. Line capacity is a scarce resource.
7. Short turnrounds are a key to utilisation.
8. Good performance is vital.
9. Surplus facilities may be an embarrassment.
10. The customer is the best judge of what he wants.
11. The railway does not exist in a vacuum.
12. Change takes time.

Below:
At the beginning of the 1990s, it was proposed that a new InterCity station should be built for Birmingham, at Heartlands on the Stechford to Aston line. This would enable trains to bypass New Street and an interchange to be built with the CrossCountry route to Derby. This too could avoid New Street. A pair of Class 37s from the King's Norton direction head for Water Orton. On the high level, the route is to Stechford, left, and Aston, right. The date is 12 May 1992. *Author*

'Railtrack co-ordinates train services and grants train operators access to the rail infrastructure, which it is responsible for maintaining and in which it invests. It oversees the safety of the operational network under the supervision of the Health and Safety Executive.' (Department of Transport, 1994).

The Track and its Maintenance

To construct a railway, the route has to be levelled, and the earthworks, bridges and tunnels completed. In the majority of cases this work was achieved in the 19th century, but the standards then set in terms particularly of curvature and gradients remain with little change today. This constitutes the formation, on which the rest is built.

The components of railway track consist of the ballast, the sleepers, the rails and their fastenings, with all the additional elements represented by points and crossings.

Layers of ballast are placed on top of the formation. Their purpose is to spread the load imposed by the weight and movement of trains, to hold the track in place horizontally, to carry off the rainwater, and to give the track some elasticity in the vertical plane to prevent the ride experienced on trains being too 'hard'. It should also be capable of being packed beneath the sleepers to maintain levels. Ballast on the busiest lines usually consists of crushed

3.

Track and signalling

limestone or granite to a depth of at least 300mm.

Ballast is also used on curves to provide superelevation and raise the outer rail above the inner. This counteracts the centrifugal forces and allows the curve to be taken at a higher speed than would otherwise be possible. The degree of superelevation is dependent on the curve radius and the likely speed of trains using it.

The sleepers spread the wheel loads over the ballast, hold the rails to gauge, and must not allow the track or themselves to move as a result of traction or other forces. Today, prestressed and pre-tensioned monobloc concrete sleepers are found most frequently. They have a life of about 50 years.

The purpose of the rails is:

• to act as a hard unyielding surface to carry a rigid tyred vehicle;

Left:
The West Coast electrification in some ways still seems quite recent, but this view of a southbound freight headed by Stanier Class 5 4-6-0 No 44715 over the then new flyover at Rugby shows that it was indeed nearly 40 years ago.
BR/Author's collection

• to act as a beam and transmit the vehicle load to the sleepers (via a resilient pad);
• to interact with the wheels to assist in steering the vehicle in the right direction.

Rails may also be required to carry return currents for traction, or for track circuits in the signalling system. Rails today are generally of the continuously welded variety (cwr) and may be expected to last about 25 years. They are of flat-bottomed section, a design which provides great lateral stiffness.

The standard rail fastening is the PANDROL clip, which is anchored directly to the sleeper. The clip holds the rail upright and prevents it from moving longitudinally.

This brief description of the principal permanent way components in turn allows their maintenance requirements to be considered. The basic maintenance operations are designed to keep the ballast tamped to make sure that the sleepers remain properly bedded, to keep the track to accurate line, level and cant, to keep rail fastenings tightened, to examine the rails for flaws, to keep ballast clean and to keep the track drains unblocked.

Track maintenance is largely mechanised, but this requires engineering possessions during which the work can be carried out. These can and indeed must be preplanned,

although there is always a risk of some emergency work being needed. There is a requirement for strategically placed sidings at which track machines may be kept when not in use, as well as depot facilities for their maintenance.

There is also a fleet of specialised engineering wagons; this includes wagons for the conveyance of ballast (and its discharge), rail and sleepers. These wagons still go under the old telegraphic code names associated with the sea. Thus one may still find a Grampus, Mermaid, Dogfish or Walrus in the wagon fleets. Such names are far more memorable than the TOPS computer codes.

Electrification

Of the 16,500km route network on Railtrack, 30% is electrified. Around 65% of this is on the 25kV ac 50Hz overhead system, first introduced experimentally between

Lancaster, Morecambe and Heysham in 1953 (line closed 1966) and subsequently adopted as the new standard for Britain. Initial major applications were to the suburban services from Liverpool Street and Fenchurch Street, in Glasgow, and for the West Coast main line. These all followed from the 1955 Modernisation Plan proposals.

Overhead line equipment (OLE or OHLE) consists of a contact wire suspended by a catenary wire which is, in its turn, supported by a complex system of suspension cables, arms and tensioning devices. The equipment is fed from sub-stations. The greater part of the suspension system is electrically live and carried on insulators. The height of the contact wire is normally between 4.7m and 5.1m above rail level, but at low bridges it may be as low as 4.2m and at public level crossings it is increased to 5.6m. The retractable pantograph carried on the roof of electric trains to collect the current from the contact wire is tensioned. This enables it to cope with these wide variations.

The remaining electrified railways are on the long-established third rail 750V dc system, which dates from 1903/4 in Merseyside and 1915 on the present Railtrack network south of the Thames. Vestiges of third rail operation remain on the London area lines presently operated by Silverlink Metro, to North Woolwich and to Watford Junction.

Pick-up shoes on the train bear on the conductor rail. These enable the train to pick up the current from a conductor rail on either side. Conductor rails are positioned 50mm-75mm above the height of the running rails, and are normally found on one side of the running rails only. The opposite side of the line to station platforms is favoured wherever possible, to minimise the risk of electrocution of anybody falling from the platform. Gaps in the conductor rail are unavoidable at junctions, but the length of all motive power should be enough to ensure that at least one pick-up shoe remains in contact with the conductor rail at all times. Should the train stop at a point where contact is not maintained, assistance will have to be sought to move the train until that contact is restored; in such circumstances the train is said to be 'gapped'.

Sub-stations convert alternating current to the direct current supplied to the conductor rails.

In both the ac and dc systems, current return is through the running rails. All other electrification systems have now been eliminated, other than on sections of line where London Underground also operates.

The extension of electrification on the overhead system brings with it the difficulties of achieving adequate structural clearances as bridges and tunnels may be too low. In such cases, some reconstruction will be necessary, coupled perhaps with some judicious lowering of the track bed. These are matters for which the requirements in any particular case can be determined only by detailed survey. The overhead masts and catenary may also be considered intrusive in an environmental sense, and extra care may need to be taken in sensitive areas. These include stations such as Paddington which also have the perhaps doubtful privilege of being classified as listed buildings.

Left:
The re-doubling of the 19-mile single-track section between Princes Risborough and Bicester North saw a Class 08 diesel shunter and a train of track panels at work on a wet Good Friday, 10 April 1998. *Author*

Centre left:
A Personnel carrier is kept at the side of the line at Llanrwst North on the Conwy Valley line; it was seen here on 7 May 1999. *Author*

Below left:
The forthcoming Woodhead electrification, with some overhead supports already in place, sees the demolition of an overline bridge. Construction of a new ferro-concrete bridge will enable the crossing in the foreground to be removed. The location is the Penistone end of Thurgoland tunnel, 23 January 1947. The railway is now closed completely.
LNER/Author's collection

Right:
Sandite is a paste spread on the track during the leaf fall season to aid adhesion. Sandite unit No 977858, previously a single-unit Pressed Steel DMU, No 55024, waits to be overtaken by a passenger service at West Ruislip on 12 November 1998. *Author*

On third-rail schemes, the introduction of electrification is unlikely to result in any substantial clearance problems. A more problematic area is the conductor rail. Protection by the provision of secure fencing is an absolute necessity, with additional care taken where the public have access to the railway to cross it at grade.

In order to keep the capital costs of electrification schemes down, their introduction is usually accompanied by a reconsideration of the track layouts required. Thus the extension of electric services from Cambridge to King's Lynn was accompanied by the singling of a 10-mile section of line from Littleport to Downham Market and again over the six miles from Watlington to the outskirts of the terminus. There are clearly advantages in carrying out such work as part of the same programme, which extends to matters such as the condition of the track. There is little point in carrying out major electrification schemes if the state of the underlying infrastructure, for instance the condition of the drainage, is such that it will soon need substantial attention. The down side of this though is that 'electrification' easily assumes all sorts of costs with which it is only indirectly associated.

In addition, electrification is commonly linked with resignalling, since the avoidance of electrical interference with the existing system is a prime requirement.

Electrification offers cheaper, faster and more reliable operation. With better acceleration, lines can also accommodate more trains — but it can only be justified where traffic is dense. Railtrack feels that there are few places left in this category where electrification might be extended (other than for local infilling).

However, the Great Western main line is being examined for possible electrification. It is already electrified from Paddington as far as Heathrow Airport Junction, and if the CrossRail scheme should ever be progressed, that will be extended to Reading. A second element is the acceptability of diesel traction; only electric trains are permitted to use the BAA stations under Heathrow Airport, and such restrictions may apply to a Terminal 5 station, if built. Similar constraints may affect other enclosed railways in urban areas, in the future if not at present.

Track Gauge

The track gauge used throughout Britain and most of continental Europe, on what might be termed the national rail network, is 4ft 8½ in (1.435m). This is the distance between the inner faces of the two running rails. Other track gauges may be found, both broader and narrower. From a British point of view, the most significant is that in Ireland of 5ft 3in (1.6m) and that of the many narrow

313 UNITS PAN UP

Electric trains raise pantograph before proceeding

DANGER

Passengers must not cross the line or pass this point

Do not touch the live rail

Above:
Dual electrification systems need to remind drivers to make the change, and in this case it is 'Pan up'. The location is Acton Central on the North London line on 27 October 1998, looking towards Willesden Junction. The third rail ends here. *Author*

be obtained.' But the effort needed to tranship goods at places such as Gloucester, where the broad and standard gauges met, plus the chaos which resulted, spelt the end for the broad gauge. It was abolished finally in 1892.

As an island nation, gauge compatibility has not been a significant problem for Britain with international traffic. However, while train ferries operated from both Dover and Harwich for many years before the opening of the Channel Tunnel, it does perhaps explain why no similar facility was ever provided for Ireland.

Loading and Structure Gauges

The dimensions of the trains must be such that they can be run, with adequate clearances and in safety, over the railway infrastructure for which they were built. Conversely, the infrastructure must be constructed in such a way that it can accommodate the trains which the operators wish to run upon it.

This is clearly a mutual relationship. The whole is complicated by the different practices of the various British railway companies in Victorian times to the extent that they adopted different standards, the often substantial further differences seen generally in Europe, the peculiarly British practice of providing high-level passenger platforms, and the growth in dimensions of intermodal freight vehicles in general and the height of containers in particular.

A further element to be taken into account is the difference between the loading gauge of a stationary vehicle on straight and level track, and what is known as the swept envelope. This latter includes also the dimensional effects of suspension systems, allowances for tolerances and wear, the accuracy of track alignment, levels and gauge, the end and centre overhangs which are experienced with the longest vehicles when negotiating curves, and the superelevation applied to the track. All of this might be interpreted as a warning not to make clearances too tight, with specific recommendations as to the matters to be considered and the clearances to be allowed.

Some of the present-day problems are now examined.

The locomotives and rolling stock of the Victorian era are long gone, and

gauge railways, formerly industrial but now for tourist use, most notably in Wales.

Track gauge compatibility is the first requirement for through-running between different railways. In Britain, Brunel's broad gauge of 7ft 0¼ in (2.14m) was the only alternative which gained the status of a major system. 'Looking to the speeds which I contemplated would be adopted on railways and the masses to be moved,' Brunel told the Gauge Commissioners, 'it seemed to me that the whole machine was too small for the work to be done, and that it required that the parts should be on a scale more commensurate with the mass and velocity to

Right:
The Stratford-North Woolwich line was closed for an extended period in 1994/5 to permit the reconstruction of Canning Town station on a new site and the building of the DLR Beckton extension station. Beyond Custom House the passenger railway becomes a single-track siding; the other line, then goods only, is now disused. Extensive trackwork is under way on 24 March 1995. The DLR Prince Regent station is located immediately to the left of this picture. *Author*

standardised dimensions have now been the rule for many years. Variations still observable tend to reflect construction to dimensions rather more generous than those which were prescribed. Thus, greater bridge and tunnel dimensions, where they exist, ease both the adoption of overhead electrification and the carriage of the larger containers.

In the earlier days, it was important to minimise gradients since locomotive power was then limited. Speeds were also relatively low, so curvature was of little consequence. Today, obtaining adequate diesel and especially electric power is not a problem, but tight curves which limit the maximum speeds attainable are a decided disadvantage.

It does, of course, depend on the location. Matters which limit speeds to (say) 50mph are of little consequence on a short suburban branch. The principal main lines are another matter.

Rebuilding of the railway over the years has often increased the radius of curves as,

for instance, at Offord south of Huntingdon on the East Coast main line. Here, the River Great Ouse has been diverted to allow a straighter alignment to be followed. The reduction in the number of tracks at many locations has enabled a straighter course to be followed by those which remain.

The Great Central Railway's London Extension featured island platforms, with the running tracks splaying out to pass either side. Unless such curves are to a very large radius, this is another source of a 'kink' in the running lines, and is a limitation on high-speed operation.

However, curvature also causes longer vehicles to overhang the track, on the outside of the curve at the vehicle ends (end throw) and across the centre of the curve in the middle (centre throw). This is a particular difficulty with passenger stock since it results in greater platform to train distances on curved platforms. The increasing attention now being afforded to disabled access highlights such difficulties, but physical constraints can make the effective solution of the problem almost unattainable.

The British platform, normally 914mm (3ft) above rail level, is a source of obstruction to many continental vehicles, since some of this space can be used for the vehicle itself when platforms are at the low levels common elsewhere. Again, fully satisfactory answers to such problems are not easily found if interoperability is to be pursued. Separate platform lines used only by British stock might be a theoretical answer, but would be very costly. Even then, protection systems would have to be instituted to prevent 'the wrong sort of train' from using them in error.

Similar problems may be caused by the positioning of underbridge girders in Britain, which occupy the same space which elsewhere on the system might be used by a station platform.

Perhaps the greatest conundrum is the much more generous dimensions of the Berne (European) loading gauge, and how far this should be replicated in Britain. There is, it might be added, nothing final about the Berne gauge other than its applicability; Eurotunnel's gauge is considerably larger still.

If rail traffic to and from the Continent grows substantially, the shortcoming of the inherited British standards will become ever more noticeable. However, it is also a domestic problem in that the height of deep sea containers is often already 9ft 6in. Will further increases take place in the next 20 years or so? Allied to this is the movement of piggyback road trailers on rail, for which increased dimensions are also necessary. At present, gauge enhancement work is being applied selectively; there is no point in raising clearances on suburban branches which see domestic passenger traffic only. But even here, with a growing custom, double-deck trains are one way of solving capacity problems...

Axle-loads

The ability of a railway to carry is dependent on the strength of the underline formation and structures. The most often used measure is that of axle-load or the weight carried by a single axle. For instance, a bogie tank wagon of 20 tonnes tare weight and a payload of 80 tonnes has a fully laden weight of 100 tonnes. This gives an axle weight of 25 tonnes, which is acceptable on a large part but by no means all of Railtrack's network. The table shows the present major categories:

Axle-loads permitted, by km of track

up to 20.3 tonnes	8.8%
20.4 to 23.4 tonnes	47.8%
23.5 to 25.4 tonnes	43.4%

The most restrictive category is confined to lines like the Cambrian Coast, those to Oban, Mallaig and Kyle of Lochalsh, Exeter-Barnstaple and sundry suburban branches in the London area. But the Isle of Wight line is recorded as being in the top category and thus able to accommodate the bogie tank wagon example. Making effective commercial use of this level of capability would be an interesting challenge, in some game designed to test management skills.

Individual structures such as bridges may have a maximum weight limit which they can bear at any one time; if so, those limitations are set out in the Appendix to the Rule Book. This has implications for double-track structures or, possibly, train lengths. Problems of this nature had a part in the decision to reduce the railway crossing the High Level Bridge at Newcastle upon Tyne from three lines to two.

Turnouts and Crossings

The simple turnout has much to commend it. This is the piece of trackwork needed for one track to diverge from or merge with another. Allied with a diamond crossing, which allows one track to cross another, these two basic items either singly or in some form of combination will allow all possible moves to be made by rail traffic. The figure right illustrates the various formations.

An assembly of turnouts is called a layout; some assemblies are sufficiently common that they have their own names. Thus a pair of turnouts between a pair of lines which allow trains to cross from one to the other is known as a crossover. This may be termed

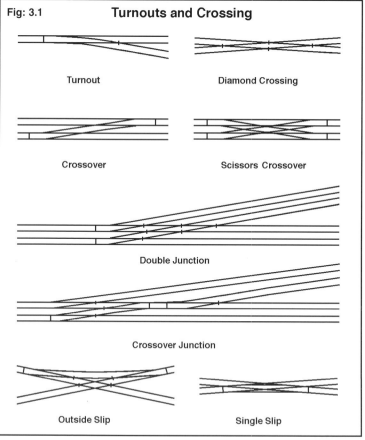

Fig: 3.1   **Turnouts and Crossing**

Turnout

Diamond Crossing

Crossover

Scissors Crossover

Double Junction

Crossover Junction

Outside Slip

Single Slip

Left:
Sharp curves result in flange squeal and wheel wear. One means of combating this is to grease the rails. This greaser is activated by the passing wheel flanges. The location is Purley, 9 February 1999. *Author*

Centre left:
A ground frame allows the train crew to set the points for the sidings, with the help of the track diagram displayed. A telephone to the signalman is provided. The location is Sinfin North, outside Derby, in 1977. In the foreground is a ramp for the Automatic Warning System (AWS). *Author*

Below left:
Litter picking is one of those necessary jobs which consume much manpower. The lookout walks along the platform at Hampstead Heath on 8 December 1998, as three men fill their plastic sacks. The team were thorough and moved remarkably quickly. *Author*

Right:
The West Coast main line on 11 October 1983 at Bletchley sees a Class 86/2 hauling the 07.40 Euston to Liverpool Lime Street. The signalbox will be replaced during the route upgrading, while the flyover in the background has now been totally disused for some time. Potentially, it forms part of the proposed east-west link being pursued by the local authorities in the area. *Author*

'facing' if these are running lines and the train making the move is approaching in the normal direction of travel, or 'trailing' (as illustrated on page 27) if access from the normal direction of travel can only be obtained by reversing the train.

Sometimes, facing and trailing crossovers may both be found in quick succession. Where there is a shortage of available length, as in the approaches to major stations, they can be made to overlap. The result is known as a scissors crossover. This requires four turnouts and one diamond crossing.

Where a double-track line diverges from another, the traditional arrangement consists of two turnouts and one diamond. This is known as a double junction, However, diamonds have been less favoured in more recent times where higher speeds are involved, since they provide too many interruptions in the rail surface. In the alternative layout to fulfil the purpose of a double junction, the diamond crossing is replaced by two turnouts, making three in all. It then becomes a crossover junction.

An outside slip consists of two turnouts and a diamond in close proximity, to allow trains to proceed from one line to another as well as make a straight crossing movement. An inside slip permits the same movements but in a more confined space; it also requires fewer components. A more complex arrangement, not illustrated, is the double slip, which allows a trains approaching from

any direction to proceed to either of the exit directions.

There has been considerable simplification of track layouts over the years. In part this is due to the fewer movements to be made when multiple-units replace locomotive-hauled passenger trains, but also the greater flexibility in routeing which can be achieved with modern signalling systems. Another reason is increasing line speeds, and there are maintenance benefits from repositioning crossovers and junctions on straight track. Higher speeds may also be required on the crossovers themselves, especially when this is a movement (say) between the slow and fast lines of a four-track railway.

Many track layouts now consist almost entirely of simple turnouts with diamonds. If it is essential to use them, diamonds may be of the switch diamond variety. Swing nose crossings in turnouts may also be used to reduce the breaks in the rail surface.

Ancillary equipment includes point heaters, mostly electric but sometimes gas powered, to keep the moving parts free from ice and snow in winter conditions.

A frequently found safety feature in track layouts is the trap point. This is normally situated to protect running lines, should a train start away from a loop or a siding leading to them without authority. A full turnout may be positioned so that the errant train is deflected away from the running line. It will be derailed clear of the track or, if a sand drag is also provided, be stopped without being derailed.

The trap point is only set for the running line when the signals are cleared for that movement to take place.

Track Layouts

There are two basic methods of arranging a four-track railway, of which tandem working is probably found the more often. In this layout, tracks are laid out down fast, up fast, down slow and up slow. Examples on main lines leaving London include the Midland line from St Pancras and the Great Western main line from Paddington. On the Great Western, trains are never slow, and the slow lines are known here as the relief lines! Various nomenclatures may be found, but all imply some form of speed differential.

The tandem working arrangement separates the express passenger services from the suburban passenger and local services. At the terminals, this is convenient for reversing trains and keeping the passenger facilities for each service type grouped together. Splitting an eight-car train into two four-car units or joining them up again is that much simpler. Away from the terminal it does, however, result effectively in two parallel railways. Movement of trains between fast and slow lines for traffic regulation purposes can be achieved only by obstructing the intermediate line while the crossing movement takes place. While it can be argued that such moves should be the exception rather than the rule, there are always the problems caused by track maintenance work which require partial line closure.

The alternative arrangement is parallel working, with lines arranged down slow, down fast, up fast and up slow. Examples on main lines leaving London include the Great Northern main line from King's Cross, north of Holloway and the South Western main line from Waterloo, west of Earlsfield.

In both these cases, the tandem arrangement applies in the London terminal area, but flyovers are used later to create the parallel arrangements. In the case of the Great Northern, a further flyover is used at the outer terminal of the inner-suburban services. Thus, south of Welwyn Garden City, a flyover enables all these trains to terminate on the west side of the line.

By having lines in parallel, trains may easily be routed from fast to slow lines or slow to fast, provided of course that suitable

crossovers have been installed. The arrangement is inherently more flexible than the tandem layout already discussed.

In practice, the track arrangements which have been provided historically tend to survive. Slow lines are likely to be just that in terms of being subjected to a lower line speed. This will be dictated by matters such as platform positioning, which affects the geometry and thus the straightness of the track alignments. In any event, line capacity on a multiple-track railway is maximised by separating trains with different performance characteristics and, as far as possible, keeping like with like.

A further consideration is the incidence of junctions. Thus, on the main line out of Waterloo, flyovers or diveunders may be found for the divergence in succession of the line to Epsom (at Raynes Park), to Shepperton (at New Malden), both to Hampton Court and to Guildford via Cobham (at Surbiton), and so on. Grade separation in this manner allows the diverging movements to be made without affecting traffic in the opposite direction in any way. Construction, however, is relatively costly, and there must be the physical space available for the work to be undertaken.

On one of the busiest junctions on the South Western main line at Woking, where the line to Portsmouth diverges, a flat junction is provided. In part, this reflects the practical impossibility of building the approaches to a flyover (or diveunder) through the station platform area. This can only be achieved if, as on the independent goods lines at Crewe, trains do not require to call at the station concerned. Woking is one of the top revenue-earning stations in the area, and bypassing it would not make good business sense.

The four-tracked railway is found only where traffics are dense, and the double-track line may perhaps be considered the standard conventional arrangement. Here, all trains must be accommodated on the two running tracks, and overtaking of one train by another needs the provision of a passing loop as a minimum. Sometimes this will be found associated with a station platform but in industrial areas as in, for instance, South Wales, goods loops are found. The description 'Goods lines' implies that this section of track is not suitable for use by passenger trains, without additional signalling precautions being taken.

Despite the benefits of grade separation at junctions where the line occupation is high, there are far more flat junctions in existence. More than one parallel movement may be possible at any one time, but often this is not so. This depends on the layout of the junction itself, the signalling provided, and of course the nature of the moves to be made. There has been a tendency in recent years to simplify junction provision by the use of fewer and more standardised permanent way components. While this may achieve useful economies, there is also likely to be some reduction in capacity.

In the consideration of track layouts so far, it has been assumed that each main running track is unidirectional. There have always been exceptions, both in yards and in station areas, as well as in the special case of a single-track line. However, bi-directional signalling is becoming more common. Where this is introduced, the direction of operation can be reversed on one or both tracks. Provided that suitable crossovers are also put in place, this offers more flexibility to cope with uneven demand levels and to circumvent problems caused, for instance, by a train failure.

The simplest form of railway has a single line only. Access to the single-line section is controlled by the signalling system on the principle that one train only is allowed to occupy the section at any one time. The capacity of a single-line railway is critically dependent on the number and frequency of passing places. The simplest form is a single-track passenger branch, where there is a separate platform at the junction station and the branch train does nothing other than shuttle to and from the branch terminus. Among the simplest examples is the Stourbridge Junction to Stourbridge Town branch in the West Midlands.

Case Study: The Stourbridge Town Branch

The single-car Class 153 unit brakes as it arrives at Stourbridge Town at 13.56. This PTE station was rebuilt in 1996 on a new site, a little further from the town centre which can be seen in the distance. The train is the 13.53 from Stourbridge Junction, which has connected out of the 12.27 from Stratford-upon-Avon via Snow Hill and the

13.11 from Great Malvern to Birmingham New Street. An extended Stourbridge bus station, beyond, now occupies the former railway station site. This is integrated transport.

With a steeply graded branch of a little more than half a mile, the dedicated Class 153 makes 80 return trips every weekday, with up to five of those trips being accomplished in each of the busiest hours. The line owes its continuing existence to the need to provide access to Stourbridge Junction from the town centre. The Junction station offers a basic four trains an hour to Birmingham Snow Hill and beyond, and one to New Street. In the other direction, services run twice an hour to Kidderminster and Worcester, with some extended to Great Malvern and Hereford.

The branch service is nothing if not comprehensive. The first train from Stourbridge Town is at 05.47 and the last one arrives back at 00.01. Three minutes are allowed for the journey, so the train is on the move for no less than eight of those hours. There are no Sunday services.

However, the Class 153 still manages no more than about 100 miles of revenue-earning service in a day, to which has to be added ferrying the empty unit 16 miles each way to and from Tyseley. Are there any more effective ways in which the branch could be operated? Both Central Trains and Travel West Midlands, the principal bus operator in the area, are part of the National Express Group.

Signalling and Train Control

Railway signalling is a prime requirement of operation, both for determining the capacity of the network and for the operation of that network in safety.

Steel wheel on steel rail has proved over the years to be a most effective combination, and is the basis of the railway as we presently know it. Early fears that it would cause insuperable adhesion difficulties proved largely unfounded, though there can still be problems, especially in the leaf fall season and in icy conditions. However, it does not have the stopping ability of rubber tyre on tarmac, and 500 tonnes of train travelling at 125mph is a formidable object. It will take about one mile before it can be brought to a halt, even with a full brake application.

In the formative years of railways, speeds were low, trains were light and traffic infrequent, but it was still necessary to have a means of indicating to locomotive drivers whether they had permission to proceed. This task was performed initially by the railway policeman, who gave a starting signal to the driver by using the position of his arms. Later, he used a mechanical arm attached to a fixed post. But although it might have been safe to leave one station for the next, once (say) 30min had elapsed since the previous train left, what might have happened to it? If the train had broken down or come to a standstill for any reason, a rear end collision was at least a possibility.

If it could be confirmed that the previous train had arrived at the next station before the subsequent train was allowed to leave, this would be a great advance. This became the province of the electric telegraph, which had only recently been invented. Bell signals were also introduced to enable precise messages to be exchanged. The need to avoid any ambiguities became apparent very early on. Thus was borne the signalling principle of the absolute block — of being absolutely certain that there was no more than one train in any one signal block, or section, at any one time.

Meanwhile, stations and yards were growing in their capacity, and more train movements were being made within them.

Rather than have more policemen scattered around the area, who after all had to find a way of communicating with each other, the next move was to concentrate such operations in a single building. The signals could be controlled from this 'signalbox' with mechanical wire linkages worked by a lever, and by one man. But the signalman also needed to control the points to ensure that contrary indications were not given. From this stemmed the interlocking of points and signals, another key advance.

Increasing speeds heralded the introduction of the distant signal, to give the driver advance warning of the need to stop at the subsequent home (stop) signal. Another was the concept of the overlap. This requires an unobstructed distance to be maintained beyond a stop signal, as a precaution against the driver failing to stop. Point locks on facing points (those encountered which can change the direction taken by an approaching train, as opposed to trailing points) became compulsory, as did a number of other measures.

Coupled with the evolving signalling regulations, with statutory enforcement from 1889, this became the basis of railway signalling throughout Britain for many years. But it was not without its problems:

- The area a signalman could control was limited by the mechanical linkages and the brute force needed to operate them, as well as by the area which he could see.
- The signalman had little intimation of traffic approaching him but not yet in his area of control. He thus had limited room for manoeuvre to minimise the effects of potential conflicts.
- The visibility of the semaphore signal was seriously reduced in adverse weather conditions, especially fog.
- Staffing and maintenance costs were high.

The signalmen's areas were extended by the introduction of some electric operation of distant points and signals, but a more significant advance was the birth of the

Right:
Where a track is little used, dirt and grease can make the operation of track circuits uncertain. In such circumstances, a wire is welded to the top of the rail surface; this increases the pressure of the wheel and much improves the chances of its presence being detected. In view of the diesel fuel on the sleepers, the precautions are well justified. This is Llandudno Junction on 7 May 1999. *Author*

Centre right:
Large signalboxes of the traditional type are now rare, even if what they contain is rather more modern. This is the box at Stockport Edgeley on 16 March 1999. *Author*

Below right:
A panel box interior, this one being at Temple Mills East. In this small panel, the signalman controls it directly rather than from a separate desk.
BR/Author's collection

Traffic Control organisations. Described in more detail later, their original form was a freight office which received telephoned reports of operations over a wide area. This allowed the controllers to anticipate problems arising from out-of-course running and instruct the signalmen on the action they should take. This might, for instance, affect the priorities given to individual trains at junctions, or the holding of a departing train to make a connection with a late-running arrival.

Signal visibility issues were eased dramatically by the colour-light signal which, in contrast to the semaphore, displays the same indications to the driver by day and by night. It has no moving parts. The colour-light can also display up to four aspects, giving red (stop), single yellow (stop at next signal, which is red), double yellow (stop at next signal but one, which is red) and green (line clear until advised otherwise). The double flashing yellow is of recent introduction, at present used sparingly at high-speed junctions.

An important part of the equipment is the track circuit, which detects the presence of a train electrically by the passage of a weak current through the two running rails. The presence of the wheel and axle combination of the train causes a short circuit, and this is used for protection purposes. This device ensures that signals in the rear of a train are held at danger and it locks the points ahead in the direction of travel. It also confirms the presence of the train to the signalman.

The way was now open for the introduction of power signalling over considerable geographical areas. Although originating in the 1930s, power boxes were introduced rapidly in the post-1955 Modernisation Plan years. With these came the NX or entrance-exit panel boxes, which are relay based. A large-scale track diagram is mounted vertically in front of a series of perhaps four of five desks at which signalmen sit. By depressing buttons on a mimic of that part of the diagram relating to the area for which each is responsible, points are changed, routes are set and signals cleared. There are separate buttons at the start and end of each section of route, hence the NX description. The precise choice of route, where there are alternatives, is left to the logic of the system, although this may be overridden. The route set is indicated by a line of white lights, which turn red as the train proceeds along the route. The train's reporting number is displayed on the diagram. Thus 2F36 is the 11.22

Above left:
The box at Leigh-on-Sea, LTS line, during single-line working on 12 January 1986. This is the view looking east towards Southend. *Peter Ashton*

Above:
The signalbox interior might sport a considerable number of levers; in this case it would appear to be around 60. This is Paddock Wood on 2 November 1960, when the Hawkhurst branch was still open. The branch train actually passed beneath the box.
*G. S. Robinson/
Author's collection*

Right:
The AWS system, as found in the cab of Bulleid 'Battle of Britain' Light Pacific No 34062 *17 Squadron*. The black/yellow disc is indicating that the line ahead is not clear. *C. F. Klapper/
Author's collection*

Paddington to Slough, where '2' refers to the class of train (local passenger) and indirectly to its priority, 'F' is the geographical area in which it terminates, and '36' is the individual train number.

The progress of trains can be scrutinised from a position behind the signalmen, which enables the scene as a whole to be monitored and alternative courses of action to be determined where difficulties arise. The power box is also the source of information for the station announcer, which can be given out with authority. Thus, at Wigan North Western: 'The train now approaching Platform 5 is the 12.32 First North Western service from Liverpool Lime Street, going forward at 13.04 to Preston, Lancaster, Carnforth, Grange-over-Sands, Ulverston and Barrow-in-Furness.'

The 1950s also saw the development and widespread installation of the Automatic Warning System (AWS). This is a complementary system to the signalling, which gives audible and visible indications to the train driver as to whether the signals which he passes display line clear (a bell sounds, black disc shown) or more restrictive indications (a horn and a yellow/black segmented disc). The driver has to acknowledge a warning horn by pressing a button to prevent the brakes from being applied automatically. It is, however, up to the driver to then control the train and obey the signals. The system is electro-magnetic in nature, using magnets set between the rails and a receiver on the train; no physical contact is made. AWS may be a fairly basic system, but it works well and achieves the task which it was set up to do. It is also reliable.

Recent installations such as Integrated Electronic Control Centres (IECCs) dispense with the large signalling panel and substitute a series of visual display units (VDUs). The timetable is entered into the computer, and the repetitive nature of many timetables

nowadays enables the signalman to control by exception rather than having to oversee every movement. Intervention by the signalman, when it is necessary, is undertaken by keyboard, while relay interlocking is now the preserve of a computer logic program (Solid State Interlocking, or SSI). The computer also drives the train describers, which identify the train and its location to the signalman, and information displays for passengers.

The future promises the introduction of moving block (or transmission-based) signalling, where the age-old concept of an exclusive block section between physically fixed signals is superseded. With moving block, an envelope is created for each train, so that at all times it is kept at a safe distance from the next. The size of that envelope is determined by matters such as the speed of the train at the time, and its braking distance. But that is still for the future.

Other changes may concern track circuits. Although invaluable in what they set out to do, track circuits do suffer from a high failure rate. Also, they may have difficulty in detecting the presence of lightweight vehicles which have only a few axles. An alternative approach is the axle-counter, which counts and records the number of axles passing a beacon and compares this with the numbers passing the next.

Line Capacity

Line capacity is a valuable and indeed a saleable commodity. It is determined primarily by the length of the block sections.

With multiple-aspect signalling (MAS), signal spacing is usually at more or less equal intervals. This gives higher capacity than traditional signalling, where signalbox spacing is, by comparison, much more varied.

A four-aspect MAS scheme will have greater capacity than a three-aspect scheme, in which the double yellow indication is omitted. The double yellow's purpose is to give train drivers an early indication that the line is clear for only a limited distance ahead, so that they can regulate their speed accordingly. A double yellow gives the driver two signal sections over which to travel before reaching the red; with a three-aspect scheme, there is only one section in-between.

With a three-aspect scheme, a brake application would normally be made only when the driver has sited the signal at yellow. Indirectly, this determines the maximum speed at which he can travel, based on the distance he requires to stop (the braking distance). A more likely result in practice is that the distance between successive signals in a three-aspect scheme will be that much greater than with four aspects, so that line speed is not unduly constrained. The loss is the consequential reduction in line capacity.

The ability to maintain speeds without interruption is an effective way of making the best use of capacity. Permanent speed restrictions impose a time penalty which is the cumulative effect of the time lost through decelerating, that at the prescribed speed,

Right:
A pair of Class 455 units with No 5863 in the lead round the corner from the bridge over the River Thames at Staines, and cross the Windsor branch junction at the west end of the station. This train will proceed to Waterloo via the Hounslow loop ; the date is 13 November 1998 . There are no grade seperated junctions on the Windsor lines but there are some routeing alternatives. *Author*

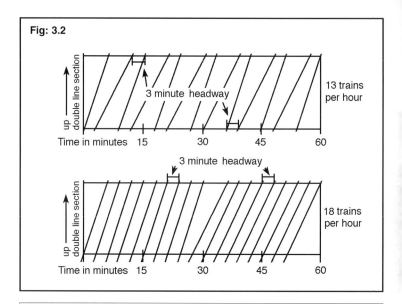

Fig: 3.2

3 minute headway

13 trains per hour

3 minute headway

18 trains per hour

Above:
Flighting of Fast and Slow Trains

Below:
Flighting of Trains on a Single Line

Right:
Platform loops keep the main lines clear to allow nonstop services to pass. This is Tonbridge, the view being that of a Eurostar bound for Brussels, passing through the station at speed on 21 September 1998.
Author

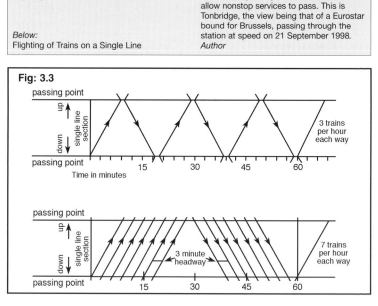

Fig: 3.3

passing point

single line section

passing point
Time in minutes

3 trains per hour each way

passing point

single line section

passing point

3 minute headway

7 trains per hour each way

and the time taken to accelerate back to line speed. Eliminating or at least minimising such restrictions can represent a worthwhile investment.

Station stops impose a similar limitation; even on an electrified suburban line, each short stop will add a couple of minutes to the overall time. Where longer distance trains are concerned, the time spent stationary will increase. Thus a Stafford stop on main line services is usually 1min 30sec.

To some extent, this can be overcome by loops at stations, as is indeed practised at Stafford. But the most effective means of maximising route capacity is for all trains on the route to maintain the same service pattern. Following that, trains can be grouped in batches of 'fast' and 'slow' services. This is demonstrated in Figure 3.2, a theoretical example where the signalling requires a minimum 3min headway to be maintained. With alternate trains fast and slow, the line capacity is 13 trains per hour (tph). If run as two separate groups, capacity rises to 18tph.

Whether the commercial requirements of the operating companies would support such a service pattern is of course another matter. This example is used to show only that line capacity is not fixed. Such calculations also of course affect freight operations.

It may be noted that Eurotunnel's access charges for the Channel Tunnel are based on a charge for the standard train path, which is defined as being equivalent to that occupied by their own shuttle services. Both faster and slower trains occupy proportionately more than one path, and incur charges accordingly. Nevertheless, two successive Eurostar trains will only occupy one path more than a single Eurostar train, though together they may occupy three. Perusal of the Eurostar timetable shows a pattern of trains from Waterloo to Paris at 23min past the hour, and to Brussels at 27min past.

The subject of access charges is not covered further in this book. They are largely a commercial matter, though as this example demonstrates, access matters may have a bearing on the availability and use of train paths.

Single Lines

Single lines have their own additional constraints to those already discussed. Clearly, the most disastrous occurrence would be for two trains to meet head on. This has resulted in the drivers of trains over single-line sections being required to carry a physical token, issued by the signalman at

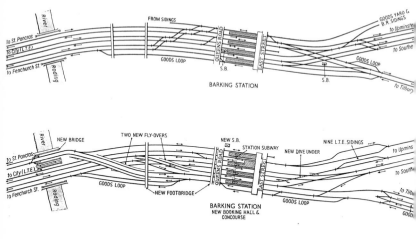

one end of the section and returned to the signalman at the other, as an authority. The token is incorporated into the interlocking system to prevent more than one being issued at any one time.

Here, too, technology has progressed, and the Radio Electronic Tokenless Block (RETB) system is in use in central Wales, in the Highlands of Scotland, and on the East Suffolk line in East Anglia. The metal token is replaced by an electronic one, which is 'issued' by radio to the driver by the signalman and displayed on a console in the cab, and 'returned' to him when the journey through the section is completed. It then reappears on the signalman's console. The whole is controlled by a computer in the signalbox, which prevents the simultaneous issue of more than one token for any section.

The points in the passing loops are set so that trains from each direction always use the same track, and this keeps them clear of each other. Hydro-pneumatically operated, they may be trailed through when trains depart the loop.

The effects of flighting trains with a single line may be even more dramatic in capacity

Above:
The arrangements at Barking until the 1950s consisted of a series of flat junctions, with numerous traffic conflicts. The rebuilding required the construction of two flyovers to the west of the station, and a diveunder to the east. This enabled the provision of cross-platform interchange between the main LTS line and the Underground in each direction. There are no conflicts at all between the Underground and other services. Also, freight between Stratford/the T&H line and the Tilbury line was grade-separated from the Underground and the LTS main. This diagram shows the layout before and after the work was carried out in 1958-9. *Author's collection*

terms. Figure 3.3 (page 38) shows how the 3tph in each direction might rise to 7tph per direction. Again, it is stressed that the model is theoretical, but the differences can be impressive.

Passenger stations and level crossings are also part of the railway infrastructure, but these are covered elsewhere in the book.

4

'There is no station more interesting than that of York. It is lofty and spacious; handsome so far as a railway station can be.' John Pendleton, Our Railways, 1894.

The railway station is the point at which the public gain access to, or leave, the railway network. It is also a place where passengers may change trains from one service to another, though this function is confined to relatively few stations. At the beginning of 1999 there were 2,499 stations on the Railtrack network, of which 14 are termed independent. These are the stations with the greatest commercial potential. They are operated by Railtrack themselves and are as follows:

Passenger Stations

Charing Cross, Euston, King's Cross, Liverpool Street, London Bridge, Paddington, Victoria, Waterloo, Birmingham New Street, Edinburgh Waverley, Gatwick Airport, Glasgow Central, Leeds and Manchester Piccadilly.

Other stations are leased by Railtrack to the Train Operating Company (TOC) which has the greatest presence there, and which itself then collects access fees from other TOC users.

Station Layout

Stations may be classed as through, at which services make intermediate calls in their journeys, or as a terminus. Termini end very firmly at the buffer stops. In practice, there

are combinations. Through stations may also have terminal bays (Rugby and Carlisle are examples), and there is nothing to prevent a train terminating in a through platform if the signalling allows. All 12 platforms at Birmingham New Street are through. Conversely, trains may enter a terminus and reverse to continue their journey; this is rare, and historic reasons such as past line closures are usually the cause. Thus, on the Marlow branch trains reverse at Bourne End, and on the Gunnislake branch at Bere Alston.

The through station on a double-track line needs a platform to serve each track. Apart from the provision of access from the public highway, passenger facilities can be minimal; it is, however, a poor station which cannot provide lighting, some basic form of shelter, an indication of the destinations served and from which platform to catch the train, and a timetable. In a small

Right:
The train shed at York lies in the background as the morning 'Talisman' leaves behind 'A4' Pacific No 60025 *Falcon* on 17 June 1957. This was the inaugural run, and the train which left King's Cross at 07.45 was due in Edinburgh at 14.30. The train set returned to London the same day. *BR/ Author's collection*

Left:
A modern station on two levels was built at Smethwick Galton Bridge and opened in 1995. Less than a month after it opened, No 150132 calls at the upper level with the 14.23 Stratford-upon-Avon to Stourbridge Junction on 13 October. *Author*

Centre left:
A wayside outer-suburban station with modest facilities, Effingham Junction sports a ticket machine on each platform. The date is 13 November 1998. *Author*

Below left:
Liverpool Lime Street main line station has the large overall roof that used to be associated with all the most important stations. A pair of units await departure on 22 November 1997. On the right is No 150140 with the 10.20 to Manchester Victoria and Rochdale. No 142058 in Merseytravel livery will form the 10.12 to Wigan North Western. *Author*

Above right:
Yeovil Pen Mill is one of those rare stations with platforms on both sides of one running line. This was the view looking north on 28 February 1989. Most southbound trains use Platform 3. *Peter Ashton*

uncomplicated passenger station, no pointwork is needed and signalling is dependent on what is required for the line as a whole.

Platforms may be of either the side or the island variety. A side platform at ground level offers direct access from the street, but only to that platform. The other will have to be reached by subway or overbridge; sometimes direct street access will be available on that side as well. There is seldom more than one ticket office, and passengers requiring tickets will need to make their way to it, wherever it is located. Occasionally, access between the platforms may be made at grade if there is an adjacent level crossing or, in a few instances only nowadays, a foot crossing.

Where the platforms are in a cutting, access may be from a bridge spanning the railway with a ticket office there. With a viaduct location, ground level access is more usual, via steps.

With the alternative arrangement of an island platform, there is no need to consider the cost of the duplication of facilities and their maintenance, and platform staff can be reduced to the minimum. However, level access from the street is most unlikely to be available, other than in conjunction with a level crossing and a walk up the ramp. This is an area which will require further consideration in conjunction with the needs of those with disabilities.

At a larger through station, platform requirements reflect the number of trains which are expected to make use of it at any one time. Usually, one train per platform is all that can be accommodated, but the notorious Platforms 1 and 4 at Cambridge (a very long through platform with each end numbered separately) has a scissors crossover at the centre point. It can easily accommodate two full length trains simultaneously, though the information systems such as public address need to be first rate. It is not unknown for Railtrack to change its mind as to which part of the platform is to be used, especially if services are running out-of-course. Passengers who position themselves wrongly may need not a brisk walk, but to run.

Another variety, relatively rare, is a track with a platform on both sides. This has the advantage that passengers can join and alight from the train on either side; this may be used as a means of separating crowds. Thus, passengers may alight only on the left side of the train, for instance, while all those waiting to join do so from the right side. With slam door stock this might be encouraged, but would be impossible to enforce. Today, with sliding door stock, the doors can be opened and closed by the train operator in a predetermined sequence.

Other arrangements may be found occasionally, usually in some historical context. Thus, at Colchester, what at first appears to be a very long platform turns out to be a Platform 3 on the south end situated on the up main line, while Platform 4 at the north end is on the up loop line. This resulted from station rebuilding in the Modernisation Plan years.

At through stations, platform loops may help traffic regulation. On the South

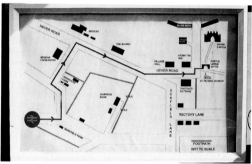

Eastern's straight double-track racing stretch over the 26½ miles between Tonbridge and Ashford, there are five intermediate stations. At three of these, platform loops give an opportunity for fast trains to overtake the stopping trains. At none of them are platforms provided on the main lines. End-to-end running times vary from 23min to 37min, which indicates the capacity constraints which the slow services can cause.

In a true urban situation, the much more confined island platforms 13/14 at Manchester Piccadilly (for services to Oxford Road and beyond) are each able to take three short trains. Both are reversibly signalled, which adds considerably to their flexibility and, occasionally, to passenger confusion.

Terminating trains are likely to need to reverse direction when they depart; in such cases it is necessary to make an assessment of how long they will be stationary. It is prudent to allow long-distance services some recovery time based on their punctuality record, and it is also an opportunity to replenish water tanks for the lavatories. Buffet stocks may also need to be supplemented. Similarly, it is a chance to give the interiors a quick sweep through to remove the litter. Seat reservation labels may need to be affixed, and new window stickers showing the calling points attached. It all takes time.

Such calculations are necessary to determine the number of platforms needed, taking into account peak and also seasonal demands, and any need to cater for special events with additional services and charters. Special trains to London destinations are always a possibility, but sporting events may produce large crowds. Paddington takes on a different air when Cheltenham Races are in progress, as does Epsom on Derby Day and White Hart Lane when Spurs are playing at home.

Football matches can bring their own problems; supporters of rival teams may have an antagonistic view of each other. Further complications arise where the paths of supporters of different sets of matches cross. The author is assured that any BT Police Officer caught studying the football fixture list in a newspaper is only doing his job and anticipating where future clashes might occur.

The results of all the deliberations on train movements at a large station form the basis of a station working document. This shows from where, when, and at which platform each incoming train will arrive, its composition, what happens next to the train itself and the train crew, and the departure arrangements.

All railway stations have their constraints, and crowd handling can be a particular problem. The principal passenger movements in a station are likely to be from the entrance to the ticket office, thence to the platform(s), also from the platform(s) to the station exit. There will of course often be other movements, notably for passengers changing trains within the station, and visiting station facilities whether they be retail shops, snack bars or lavatories. There will be those meeting arriving passengers or seeing others off. Some movements will be random, others will be predictable. However, in station design it is desirable to anticipate the main movements as far as possible. This then gives an opportunity to keep passenger flows separated from each other to avoid congestion.

This extends to the capacity of circulating areas, passages and stairways, as well as the platforms themselves. How much space is really needed around the ticket office?

Case study: Vauxhall station

At Vauxhall, the station used by South West Trains is adjacent to London Underground's Victoria Line station. There were particular problems when the Bakerloo Line was closed south of Piccadilly Circus to Waterloo and Elephant for several months in 1997. This was to allow the tube tunnels beneath the Thames to be strengthened.

In the morning peak, up main slow line trains to Waterloo call at Vauxhall Platform

7, an island platform, on a 2½ min headway. Platform 8 is used for the corresponding down services. The lack of a Bakerloo service from Waterloo resulted in many more commuters than usual transferring to the Victoria Line at Vauxhall. This meant that everybody had to descend the normally adequate but not particularly generous single set of steps in the centre of the island platform, to reach the subway. Simultaneously, others wishing to catch down line services were coming up those same steps.

The result was that the platforms were failing to clear before the following train arrived and deposited more people. At the same time, the pressure of numbers hindered the movement of others along the platform, with knots of passengers building up close to the platform edges at the top of the steps.

Such situations can be worsened if there are fast nonstopping services on the other side of the platform, when those nearest risk being severely buffeted by a 125mph train passing at line speed. Station circulating space is never unlimited; the concourse at King's Cross is quite small, and queues for trains being prepared in the platforms can only be accommodated with difficulty. To cope with this, the concourse has been marked on the ground with queuing areas.

Charing Cross is also a physically restricted station. It is very busy for suburban traffic, with a fair two-way passenger flow. Here the trick is to try and separate those arriving from those departing, to stop them from obstructing each other. This often means the use of the full-height barrier gates to prevent platform access before the previous train has cleared. But train turnrounds can be very fast, and time is limited accordingly. A further impediment are the departure displays on the concourse; departing passengers congregate there waiting for their train to be platformed.

Fortunately, a high proportion of users are regulars who perhaps have a better understanding of the quirks of the station than would a stranger.

By contrast, Waterloo main line station of 1922 has a huge concourse in between a line of offices with ticket office, shops and cafes at concourse level and facing the barrier line which serves 19 platforms directly. This station has over the years catered successfully for troop movements

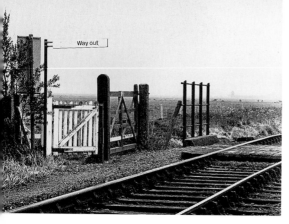

and for summer Saturday crowds waiting for the Atlantic Coast Express, as well as many commuters.

Ticketing

What makes a good ticketing system? The 'Treasury Competition' was announced in *The Times* on 6 September 1839, and the judges were particularly keen to see ideas covering four points:

- the convenience as regards public use;
- the security against forgery;
- the facility of being checked, which must of necessity be rapid; and
- the expense of the production.

This competition was, however, to do with the Post Office, not the railway. The result was the Penny Black. Nevertheless, railway ticketing systems need similar attributes, to which might be added:

- speed of issue; and
- the provision of management information.

It was indeed only two years earlier that Thomas Edmondson had produced the first board tickets of 2¼ in x 1⅙ in, individually and progressively numbered for accounting purposes and dated by the clerk in a press at the time of issue. Only in 1990 were Edmondson cards superseded generally.

Conventional railway ticketing is based on sales at the ticket office window. More windows open means less waiting time for customers, but also higher staffing costs. Too few windows, and excessive queues can

build up, and that may also congest the station concourse. Passengers who thought they had enough time to purchase a ticket but who find that they haven't, decide to abort and catch the train anyway. Penalty Fares areas bring their own problems, as well as the general revenue risk of fares evasion.

It is perhaps helpful to set out the arrangements which apply in a Penalty Fares area. A simple test applies:

- Has the passenger got a valid ticket for the whole journey being undertaken?
- If not, was it impossible for him to buy a ticket (or an authority to travel) at the start of the journey?

'Impossible' means just that, not that there was a long queue at the ticket office. An out-of-order ticket machine at an unstaffed station, with no alternative, is a valid reason.

- Were the statutory notices in place at the station of departure, warning that Penalty Fares were in operation?

If the answer to the first two questions is 'no' and to the third 'yes', a Penalty Fare is payable, except in very limited and defined circumstances. These include the journey starting outside the Penalty Fares area, in which case the passenger could not have been expected to know about the conditions.

Management needs to decide on the service standards it is seeking to provide. During the transaction at the window, the efficient ticket office clerk should be spending more time waiting for the customer,

rather than the other way round. Being completely at home with the ticketing equipment, having a thorough knowledge of the train services, and achieving accuracy and speed in money handling are key attributes. But so much depends on the customer. Most commuters know exactly what they want, and many have the right sum ready. They also leave arrival at the station until the last possible minute.

In contrast, transactions at stations frequented by overseas visitors, who have perhaps a limited command of the language and little knowledge of the railway, tend to take longer. At any large station with a wide spread of service provision types, lack of familiarity with all the services plus the ticketing alternatives of full fares, Savers, SuperSavers etc, and the associated restrictions, can make transactions lengthy. As the National Conditions of Carriage make clear, it is the customer's responsibility to make sure that he has been issued with the right ticket. Returning to the window with more questions is also a hazard. A separate enquiry facility can help.

Customers do not arrive at stations at equal intervals, and peaks and troughs of demand are apparent from time to time. Single-line queuing in which all customers wait in turn for the next available window is now more frequently found. There is also the possibility of using some windows for local tickets only, or for seasons and First Class only, and so on. This can lead to difficulties of polite but firm enforcement.

But there are other pitfalls. Ticket retailing must be impartial between the Train Operating Companies. The lead retailer, who will normally be the station operator, is not permitted by the Regulator to give his own services undue priority. Two windows for ACE trains only and one for all the other companies using the station is not allowed, without the Regulator's consent. Thus, if the company running local services is not the same as the one running long-distance services, the separation of ticket sales between windows may have other complications.

Ticket retailing may also be carried out by ticket machines operated by the passenger; some of those now in place accept debit and credit card payments as well as cash. But passenger-operated machines are at their best when the range of ticket types and of destinations served is relatively small. The purchase of return tickets for two adults and two children between Reading and Newquay using a Family Railcard, from an impersonal machine which insists on payment in either coin or bank notes (maximum £10 value) in pristine condition, defies the imagination — especially if they would like seat reservations too.

Present moves in the industry encourage advance ticket purchase by telesales for long-distance services, for the good and sufficient reason that raising load factors on trains is an economic necessity. Under this sort of regime, cheap tickets will only be available by advance purchase, and then for use only on the train and date specified. By such means, overcrowding could also be contained. However, the thrust of this book is to concentrate upon matters operational; the

main point here is the uncertain future role of the large ticket offices at major stations.

If ticket purchase in the future moves more and more away from the station environment to telesales and the internet, what level of staffing presence should be provided on railway premises for the residual ticketing function? There will always be a requirement for tickets for local journeys; advance purchase for these other than in the form of season tickets is not realistic. That, though, is perhaps where Smartcard technology will come into its own.

At the very least, staff will be needed at major stations to provide information about services, to look after passengers and to provide general reassurance.

Where stations are permanently unstaffed, or during periods when ticket offices are closed at staffed stations, ticketing presents a different set of problems. The main alternatives available at present are:

• purchase from staff travelling on the train;
• purchase at a machine situated on the platform;
• prepayment so that a valid ticket is already held.

All have their strengths and weaknesses. On-train collection promotes a staff presence, but on occasion staff may not be able to cope with the passenger volumes before reaching the next stop. Machines on the platform enable the passenger to look after his own ticketing needs, but they may be vandalised and put out of order as well as losing any cash they have taken. Machines also have to be serviced and replenished with consumable items such as ticketing rolls and print ribbons, and emptied of cash. Who checks that the passenger actually has a ticket? This is a difficulty with any prepayment system.

Information Systems

The friendly enquiry clerk, or travel consultant, which seems to be the currently preferred title, is one means of dispensing face-to-face information at stations. But this is a labour-intensive method, and duties may include the issue of reservations and travel tickets as well.

Such transactions are seldom quick, and queues can build quickly.

The presently used main alternatives for the display of timetables on posters at stations seem to be:

• Departure sheet by destination station, in order of departure times.
• Display of full timetable for route concerned, often with station at which displayed highlighted.
• None at all.

Above:
Peak periods in the London area can be busy. This is Wimbledon in June 1990, and the train a pair of Class 455 units on the Kingston roundabout services which end up back at Waterloo. *Author*

Right:
The panelling of the ticket hall at St Pancras is still a mild surprise, but it appears to function perfectly adequately. Three customers, no queues. This was on 13 September 1983, but little has changed since. *Author*

The aim here should be to inform, but also to present the information in such a manner that it cannot easily be misconstrued. Full timetables allow those interested to work out other aspects of their journey and, if they also include the reverse direction, to find out the times of return trains. On the other hand, those who are put off even by the thought of reading a timetable would clearly vote for the departure sheet.

The third traditional method is public address systems, which can offer standard announcements as trains arrive, or can be used to inform those waiting of service interruptions or any special events affecting train services such as forthcoming engineering works. Public address can be seen as an environmental disaster, particularly late in the evening or at night, by those living within earshot

Then there are the basic information items, which are easily overlooked. The following is extracted from the 1950 'Requirements' book issued by the then Ministry of Transport:

Information

Welcome to Longbridge

This station is operated by Central Trains Limited.

The ticket office at this station is open:

Monday to Friday	06.00 to 24.00
Saturday	06.00 to 24.00
Sunday	09.00 to 24.00

It is our aim that you should not have to queue at the ticket office window for longer than 3 minutes at off peak periods and 5 minutes at peak periods. Under normal circumstances the peak times at this station are 07.00 to 09.30 and 16.00 to 17.00 Mondays to Fridays.

The following principal services are available from the ticket office at this station:

- ☐ Rail tickets from this station to all stations in England, Wales and Scotland served by the national rail network.
- ☐ Rail tickets from other stations in England, Wales and Scotland.
- ☐ Rail tickets from this station to stations in Northern Ireland and the Republic of Ireland.
- ☐ Seat and cycle reservations where available.
- ☐ Railcards, Rover tickets and local timetables.
- ☐ Train times for England, Wales and Scotland.

'Names of stations to be shown as conspicuously as possible on boards, buildings and platform lamps. Platforms should be adequately lighted. A clock to be provided at every station, in some conspicuous position visible from the platforms or concourse.'

At major stations, the large mechanically-worked departure indicators have long been replaced by Solari flaps and now, increasingly, by LED displays. The objective here is to provide comprehensive information to anyone on the concourse within sight of it; crucially, the departure platform is also displayed. Similar displays can also cover train arrivals for the benefit of those meeting passengers.

On a smaller scale, video screens may provide detailed information at individual platform entrances at a large station and at many smaller ones. These may also indicate whether the train is running to time. Such information is most likely to be sourced from the signalling system, but other alternatives are becoming available.

Above left:
What facilities does your station ticket office offer, and when is it open? This exemplary 1997 notice at Longbridge gives full details, including the hours of opening to midnight *on every day of the week. Author*

Left:
If it wasn't for the use of the 24hr clock, one might imagine that this picture was taken longer ago than 1969. The location is Rochdale on the Lancashire & Yorkshire Railway. But the signing is informative and it worked. The hand, which folds back into the indicator when not in use (with another on the other side) is a nice touch. *Author*

Above right:
Passengers are becoming used to platform indicators which tell one when the next train is due, but this is the first time the author has come across an indication of the train length. The location is Hamilton Square on Merseyrail Electrics, 21 October 1998. This helps ensure that passengers stand in the same parts of the platform that the train will stop. *Author*

	Destination	Time Due	Train Length
1st	West Kirby	1 min	3 car
2d	New Brighton	6 mins	3 car
3d	West Kirby	15 mins	3 car

Increasingly, stations are being equipped with a freephone means of enquiring about train running information.

Accurate and timely information is important to passengers. The author had occasion to travel to London recently from a wayside station on a double-track line, to which he had not been for many years. It was 18.30 on a Sunday evening; the ticket office was not staffed, but about 20 people were waiting for a train. What train? Where to? The tv screen was completely blank. The only timetable on display was that for the period which expired the previous day. The PERTIS (Permit to Travel Ticket Issuing Machine) refused to accept any coin at all, and both clocks forlornly displayed 14.50. Furthermore, both lines here are equipped with bi-directional signalling. Four minutes before the London train was due, the signal at the end of the down platform turned green for the London direction, that on the normal up line remaining resolutely at red. What was the chance of the London train's arrival precipitating a quick dash over the footbridge for all the passengers, some of whom would have had to cover quite a distance to reach the steps?

As matters turned out, the 18.42 departure arrived on time at the normal up platform, but such incidents hardly suggest that the white hot heat of technological revolution had reached this part of the railway.

Connections Between Trains

What constitutes a connection? To suggest that every train should, at major stations, connect into every other train is perhaps somewhat fanciful.

Connections from everywhere to everywhere suggest periods of great activity, followed by periods of quiet. Investigations have suggested that timetables of this nature as attempted in Switzerland under the Bahn 2000 scheme would be very difficult to implement, requiring as they do a more or less standard running time for trains between each and every specified formal interchange point. A further problem arises in that they would lead to low infrastructure utilisation, since all the facilities would be required in the busy period and few at other times.

Several other factors emerge:

• Where connections represent a continuation of travel in much the same direction, there is much to be said for linking up the services and avoiding the need for changing trains. Examples include Sunderland-Newcastle-Carlisle-Dumfries, or Crewe-Shrewsbury-Hereford-Cardiff-Swansea-Milford Haven. This approach was pioneered by Regional Railways.

• The importance of any interchange is dependent upon the alternatives. Passengers connecting into a train which proceeds to a port where it connects again into a once-daily ferryboat service are among the most vulnerable. The priorities for making such connections rank highly, and passengers need assurance that this is so.

• The effectiveness of connections depends upon realistic interchange times and keeping walking distances to the practical minimum. Here, cross-platform interchanges are the most successful, if they can be achieved. Interchanges are also dependent, crucially, upon punctuality and on information as to where to go.

• The need to make specific connections evaporates as service frequencies increase; there is little need to time oneself when services run (say) every 10min — except for the last train of the day.

• Trains from different lines which themselves run within two or three miles of each other are unlikely to produce any interchange passengers, since a bus would be much quicker and more direct. At any main interchange point the principal movements between trains will become known, and the volumes can be examined further from ticket sales data, head counts and market research.

All the above assumes that passengers wish to change to another train. If the transfer is to

or from a bus, other practical problems arise. Thus, how do all the staff concerned find out what is going on? If the bus driver needs to delay his departure for 2min to connect with a late-running train, who is to tell him to do so and how long he might have to wait? Out of sight of the platforms, he might just go, assuming that there are no more takers. This leads into the contractual matrix of the responsibilities of the different parties, and penalties for non-performance of the task specified.

The situation becomes more difficult still when there is no formal association between the bus company and any TOC. Making and maintaining 'connections' is always a two-edged sword; is a bus company more interested in taking people home from work with a 17.40 departure for those who finish at 17.30, or collecting a few from the railway station whose train doesn't arrive until 17.45? There is always a risk of compromise satisfying nobody.

When it comes to day-to-day operations, should the operator delay a train or bus with, say, 50 people already on board for the sake of two more whose incoming connecting service is running 10min late? And whether the reader answers yes or no in this instance, at what point will he or she draw the line?

Perhaps the most difficult area is that the local manager who has to take the decision probably doesn't know whether there are 15 passengers wanting to make the connection on that occasion, or none at all.

This is not an area which lends itself to right or wrong answers. The above discussion is aimed at exposing the background to some of the difficult decisions which have to be made, and might then be related to local circumstances.

Station Access

The simplest station has but one platform and minimal facilities, with level access from the street. The more typical double-track station with two side platforms, or more extensive stations, create more difficulties:

- Where should the station entrance(s) and exit(s) be situated?
- Where should the ticket office be positioned?
- How are passengers to gain access to each platform?
- What additional provision is necessary if the mobility handicapped are to gain access?
- Should the station feature manned ticket barriers, automatic ticket gates, or neither, and what are the staffing implications of each?
- What scale of facilities should be provided for those arriving or departing on foot, by bus, by taxi, by kiss-and-ride, by park-and-ride, or by bicycle?

In most cases, the answer will tend to be 'as it has always been done' and there may be little real choice, but these are matters which should be re-examined from time to time. Access from a street entrance on an overbridge is usually by steps, but ramps are an alternative to cater also for disabled users. The problem here is first the extensive provision costs due to the length of ramp needed, and the resulting additional time taken by the able-bodied to reach the platform. Lifts may be an alternative, but there are associated capital and maintenance costs. There is also the problem of what happens if (or when) the station is unstaffed, though the Docklands Light Railway seems to have come to a workable arrangement. It should also be remembered that features which help the disabled will also assist mothers with pushchairs and those carrying heavy cases or shopping.

Automatic ticket gates result in a staffing requirement, but this is also likely to give the staff some time to look after the customers. Answering customer queries and giving help on using the railway, while at the same time providing reassurance, will become much more achievable. To be fair, the conventional manned barrier can have much the same effect. In either case, what happens when the station is unmanned?

Facilities for passengers in the station forecourt or similar will depend upon the physical space which is or can be made available, and the problems experienced. A combination of terminating double-deck buses doing three-point turns to reverse, commuter cars trying to get into the station car park, with kiss-and-riders depositing their passengers wherever they think fit, and a taxi firm in the corner, leaves precious little room for the pedestrian who asks for nothing but a safe footway into the station. Could this description fit *your* station? If so, what can be done about it?

Any proposals for change in the station access conditions will need the agreement of all TOCs concerned and Railtrack, and also the Rail Regulator.

Station Classification

Railtrack has initiated a designation of stations and a specification for each. There are 29 Category A stations, described as those which are part of the national hub. Examples include Birmingham New Street and Glasgow Central.

There are 64 Category B stations which have a regional hub function. Darlington, Newport and Watford Junction qualify for this status. The next group are important feeder stations, Category C. There are 244 of these, and their numbers include Manchester Oxford Road, Motherwell and

Southend Victoria. These three groups together account for 13% of the total.

There are 295 stations in the next group, Category D, the medium-sized staffed station. Caerphilly, Lichfield Trent Valley and Sydenham are the bedfellows here. By far the greatest numbers fall in the small station categories. Category E is the small staffed stations, which includes Gospel Oak, Llandudno Junction and Lockerbie among its considerable numbers of 679 in total. The last Category F, the unstaffed small station, with 1,188 among its numbers or 48% of the total, includes Bishop Auckland, Cromer and Tywyn. It might be added that although a station may be staffed, that does not imply that staffing covers all the hours during which it is open for traffic. Single-shift coverage is commonplace, certainly in Category D, whereas many stations are open for a day which may extend for 18hr or more in total.

Stations are rated by Railtrack for:

- Accessibility — Platform length, unassisted disabled access and disabled toilets.

- Comfort and convenience — Sheltered waiting accommodation, waiting rooms and toilets.

- Integrated transport — Car parking, bus and light rail interchanges, taxi ranks and cycle racks.

- Information and communications — Customer information systems, public address, help points and pay phones.

- Safety and security — cctv coverage, lighting, antislip floors and handrails in subways and on footbridges.

Left:
Bicycle usage to get to the station is increasing, but no rail operators want to encourage such unwieldy machines on to their trains if they can fill them profitably with passengers. Tonbridge, seen here on 21 September 1998, has substantial provision for secure bicycle parking made by Connex South Eastern. *Author*

For accessibility, Category A stations score best at 78% fulfilling the requirements and Category B at 63%. The others hover around the 40% to 50% mark. A and B Categories do best for comfort and convenience too but Category F, the small unstaffed station, is very close behind. 75% or more of the stations meet these measures. The other categories fall into the 50% to 65% range.

When it comes to integrated transport the honours are more even, with scores of roundly two-thirds in all categories.

Information and communications elicit a score of 90% from Category A stations and this declines gradually through the categories. F stations, nearly half the total, score a dismal 30%. However, this is a difficult area since by definition these

stations are unstaffed, and total passenger
volumes are probably not enough to justify
expensive provision.

The final measure, safety and security,
produces the most even score of measures;
each of the station categories lies in the
64%-76% range. Averaging of such results is
of course open to misinterpretation; readers
will probably be able to think of examples in
any of these groups which in their opinion
fall a long way short of acceptable
standards in one way or another. But it is at
least a start.

This leads to a second point. What level
of provision is it reasonable for the public to
expect? Should lavatories be provided at all
staffed stations, for instance, and then at all
times, or only when staff are in attendance?
Come to that, how acceptable is a situation
in which virtually half the stations on the
network are unstaffed? There are some
conflicting views here. In the Passenger
Transport Executive areas, both Merseytravel
and Centro have very high proportions of
stations which are staffed. What is more,
much of the staffing is at all times that the

station is open. Elsewhere, it can be a rarity
to find anyone at all. To its credit, Metro in
West Yorkshire has had a substantial
programme in opening many new wayside
stations over the years, but there has been
no provision for staffing at all.

Reducing or eliminating staffing is
certainly a valuable means of cutting costs,
and less is needed in the way of station
accommodation and equipment such as
ticket machines. On the other hand,
unstaffed stations may be more susceptible
to the attention of vandals, and there is no-
one to issue tickets and answer enquiries.
'Well, no,' the proponents of destaffing
would argue, 'but show me a bus stop with
staff, other than at somewhere like a bus
station. If the railway is going to be
competitive on price, it has to keep its costs
down.'

To which one rejoinder might be that the
passenger journeys travelled by bus and
coach in Great Britain declined by 16% over
the decade from 1987 to 1997, whereas
rail journeys on the national network
increased by 14%. Clearly, the railway does
not wish to emulate the bus industry in this
sense. However, positive decisions to travel
by train take many other matters into
consideration apart from station staffing.

The railway industry needs to know what
passengers feel is important to them. It is
difficult to avoid the impression that personal
security now plays a rather larger part in
people's perceptions than hitherto. Whether

or not this is justified is another matter, and what is true of one area will be untrue of another. Unstaffed stations can be secluded and lonely places at which to wait by day or by night, with or without a cctv camera for company. As already recorded, Railtrack rate only 30% of these stations as having adequate information and communications.

The Section 12 Stations

Section 12 refers to the Fire Precautions (Sub-Surface Railway Stations) Regulations, 1989. Stations so defined, which does not necessarily imply underground in the conventional sense, have to meet additional conditions. Thus, Birmingham New Street is among those included, as well as the genuinely underground such as Highbury & Islington on WAGN, Argyle Street in Glasgow on ScotRail and Hamilton Square on Merseyrail Electrics. Special staff training sessions must be held, with practice evacuation sessions every six months.

Additional conditions are published in the Railway Principles and Guidance for new and altered stations. These include the need for design allowances which allow the free movement of passengers even when the station is very busy, with at least two escape routes from each platform, and the provision of smoke extraction systems.

Above left:
An emergency evacuation exercise is carried out by West Anglia Great Northern in the tunnel south of Highbury & Islington station on 20 May 1995. The unit, No 313044, has emergency steps from the cab to the four foot. *Peter Ashton*

Left:
The length of the platform at Cambridge can be judged by the stabled 12 cars on the left, and this is only halfway along the platform! This view shows the scissors crossover in the centre on 8 November 1997. *Author*

'Trains should be used for their intended purpose and should be safe for passengers, train crew and any goods carried. The design should take into account the need for compatibility with the environment, with the infrastructure, with signalling equipment and with electric traction equipment.' Railway Safety Principles and Guidance, Part 2. HSE/HMRI, 1996.

A passenger train is comprised of various items of rolling stock, each main type of which is now examined. The requirement is to move trains, which themselves may be of varying lengths (and therefore weights), to a timetable which as nearly as possible reflects the commercial wishes of the operating company.

This will dictate, or at least influence, the performance requirements.

Locomotive-hauled

The locomotive-hauled train is, in concept, as old as the railway itself. A locomotive, either diesel or electric according to route, is attached to a train of coaching stock. The total numbers of vehicles may vary according to the anticipated demand, but also by type of vehicle.

The main division of types in terms of accommodation is:

- First Class or Standard Class;
- Open or Compartment;

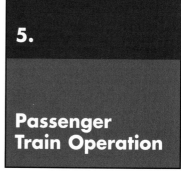

5.

Passenger Train Operation

- With or without Guard's (and van) accommodation;
- Catering vehicles;
- Sleeping Cars.

Dimensionally, all types are bogie vehicles and, roundly, either 20m or 23m in length. All vehicles need a set of buffing and

Below:
The North Wales coast still has locomotive-hauled trains, powered by EWS for First North Western trains. This requires the locomotive, here EWS's No 37426, to run round its mixed bag of Mk1 and Mk2 coaches when it gets to Holyhead. This train is the 08.10 from Birmingham New Street on 5 May 1999. *Author*

running gear, irrespective of length. To this extent, a train of eight 23m vehicles at 184m is less costly to build than nine 20m vehicles at 180m, and it will also provide more internal space for passengers. On the other hand, increasing the vehicle length also adds to the throwover problem on curved platforms, as already discussed, which opens up the gap between train and platform. Shorter vehicles will minimise this difficulty; articulation as in the Eurostar trains is one possibility. Here, each intermediate vehicle is of 18.7m length, which is still in excess of the 57ft short underframe coaches built for suburban work by British Railways in the 1950s. Again, benefits are offset by losses; a fault on an articulated unit affects the whole train until workshop attention can be arranged.

Driving Van Trailers were introduced in quantity from the 1980s. These vehicles consist of a driving cab which has time division multiplex (TDM) controls linked to the locomotive at the rear. This was not an unalloyed success at first, with its necessary use of the train lighting circuits to allow two microcomputers to talk to each other. Originally used with Class 47 diesel locomotives between Edinburgh and Glasgow, all present applications are with electric locomotives. These, or similar units, are used extensively by the Anglia Railways, Gatwick Express, Great North Eastern Railway and Virgin West Coast companies. When leading, the DVTs are not permitted to carry passengers at speeds in excess of 100mph.

Locomotive-hauled services without the DVT are flexible in the sense that a change of power is easily accomplished; it can be seen on a daily basis at locations such as Preston, where the Virgin CrossCountry Edinburgh-Brighton services exchange a Class 86 or 87 electric for a Class 47 diesel. Additional coaching stock can be added to the formation, or removed if surplus. Against this method of working is the need for facilities to release the locomotive on arrival at the terminus, or wait until another has coupled on the front and taken the train out again. The first alternative requires crossover points to the adjacent track and for that track to be unoccupied; the second sterilizes an expensive piece of kit for the length of the turnround time. In theory, the coaching stock could be removed by the station pilot to release the incoming train engine, but station pilots are very rare nowadays, if indeed they exist at all.

The DVT enables the train to be treated in a similar manner to an HST set, which consists of a power car at each end and typically eight intermediate trailers. Both can reverse direction with the minimum of fuss. The down side is the inflexibility of a formation; once set up, there it stays for an indefinite period.

This is perhaps not as limiting as it sounds. The days in which the stock of each main line train was selected individually according to its journey have long gone; today's formations have to perform a number of functions in the course of an operating day. Standard formations are thus all but essential; on Virgin West Coast, the simple task is to operate 40+ train sets in push-pull

mode, all running to/from Euston, 159 trains per day (both directions total).

It follows that the ideal stock for a prime business time departure from Euston to Birmingham may be a less suitable mix for the commuters who join the train at Coventry, or the shopping day-out to London traffic joining the train on the return journey to the capital. Such matters have to be lived with by the operator, with compromises as necessary. It is, for instance, not uncommon on some routes to see First Class accommodation downgraded to Standard or made available to Standard Class passengers for a modest additional fare.

For almost all other services nowadays, the multiple-unit reigns supreme.

Multiple-units

The multiple-units, whether electric or diesel, embody most of the benefits of the DVT/HST operations with one notable addition. This is that trains can be divided, or joined, with ease. In these multiple-unit days, train lengths are determined by the number of units making up the formation for the service. As built or adapted, diesel multiple-units may be found in one, two, three or four-car combinations, and electrics in two, three,

four or five cars. However, the diesel units are not wholly compatible with each other, while the electrics may be for ac or dc systems, or (occasionally) both.

Both the Connex franchises have a mixture of unit lengths; the SouthEastern inner services have four-car Class 465s and two-car Class 466s which can interwork freely, and SouthCentral have four-car Class 455s and two-car Class 456s. With diesel units, it depends much on what is available to the TOC concerned.

Reasons for varying the length of trains may be to serve more than one destination by division at a suitable junction station, and the equivalent combination in the reverse direction. This enables fewer train crew and train paths to be used over the common section. Thus Connex SouthCentral's xx.02 from Victoria divides at Barnham for Portsmouth Harbour and Bognor Regis and the xx.17 from Victoria divides at Haywards Heath for Bournemouth and Eastbourne.

The other principal reason is to change the train seating capacity provided during different parts of the unit diagrams. Suburban-type operations typically require greater capacity during the peaks, which involves dividing trains at the end of the morning peak and joining them up again during the afternoon. Evening services may also be reduced in formation after about 19.00 until end of traffic.

Varying formations for the latter reason has the benefit of reducing energy costs and wear and tear at times when the capacity is not needed; it also allows the unit discarded to undergo servicing and cleaning.

equip more driving cabs than would otherwise be necessary, and a combined train has no structure such as, successively, First/catering/Standard accommodation as found in the former InterCity businesses. There may or may not be passenger gangways available between (or occasionally within) units, which leads to difficulties for any on-board services, including ticket issue and inspection. But these are modest shortcomings for a concept which has proved its worth now over many years.

Multiple-units are also used extensively for long-distance services, such as:

- Edinburgh-Inverness
  ScotRail   175 miles
- Scarborough-Blackpool North
  Northern Spirit   149 miles
- Liverpool Lime Street-Norwich
  Central Trains   252 miles
- Cardiff Central-Portsmouth Harbour
  Wales & West   141 miles

However, there are also costs: dividing a train will mean that an additional crew is needed to move the second part. Another result is that trains vary in length during the operating day, and this is likely to result in uneven distribution of passengers along the length of the train. Not being certain of the length of the approaching service, passengers will 'play it safe' and assume the train will be one unit only.

The multiple-unit concept is not without its faults. There is a need to incorporate and

There are many more examples and variations. Thus, the Wales & West services above may start back from Swansea or even Haverfordwest, and run to Brighton rather than Portsmouth. All such services gain through intensive use of the units and staff, and occupy less platform space overall at points where passengers used to have to change. Run more or less on an even headway, they also provide through journey opportunities where none existed previously. Never let it be said that the railways are run

Merseyrail Electrics Wirral Services

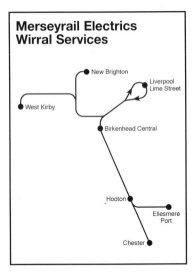

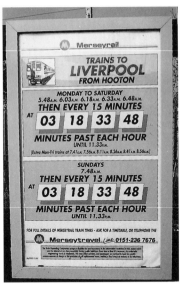

in the interests of the company and not the customer.

They also need an upgraded type of unit if passengers are expected to spend several hours in them, and this means lavatories and some form of refreshment trolley service as a minimum. Another caveat is the question of punctuality. Long journeys of this nature give additional opportunities for matters to go wrong, and punctuality needs careful monitoring. Are there any weak points in the service pattern, which show up as sources of delays? It may be possible in theory to turn round a Liverpool to Norwich service in 5min dead, but after 6hr on the move, the 25-30min actually allowed is rather more realistic. Besides, those toilet tanks need refilling.

Case study on timetable efficiency 1: Merseyrail Electrics Wirral Services

The Merseyrail Electric services arriving at Chester are allowed a 5min stand before returning towards Liverpool. Here there is a complication in that these services run every 30min, but they provide a joint operation with another 30min service as far as Hooton. This runs to Ellesmere Port and terminates there. The map shows the general layout.

However, the running time from Hooton to Ellesmere Port is 9min, rather less than the 14min to Chester. So, while the Chester turnround is cut to the practical minimum of 5min, that at Ellesmere Port is a quite generous 15min. This is unavoidable if an even interval service is to be maintained over the common section northwards from Hooton.

The resulting timetable looks like this, repeated every hour:

Liverpool Lime Street	d	04	19	34	49
Hooton	d	31	46	01	16
Ellesmere Port	a		55		25
	d		10		40
Chester	a	45		15	
	d	50		20	
Hooton	d	03	18	33	48
Liverpool Lime Street	a	29	44	59	14

This, though, is not the end of the story. As readers will appreciate, 'Liverpool Lime Street' in the table above is a euphemism for a terminal station. Lime Street is at the furthest point on the single-track Wirral services loop under Liverpool; trains cannot terminate there, but must continue in service after the time needed for an intermediate station stop only.

In succession, all trains in the above table then visit New Brighton, stand 11min, and return to Lime Street. They then take in a trip to West Kirby, stand 8min, and return to Lime Street. By now, they are again ready to take up a trip to Chester or Ellesmere Port. A complete cycle of events such as this takes 3½hr to accomplish for each train; 14 sets of trains are thus needed to provide the service as a whole. Some might feel the 11min stand at New Brighton to be excessive, but it is essential that some modest slack be built into the rolling stock and train crew diagrams or it is never possible to recover from any delays. It also provides an opportunity for litter picking. In any event, the departure time has to be fixed so that the train arrives on the loop at the right time for the subsequent working.

This is a highly efficient means of service provision; in the 210min period needed for a complete cycle, a train is on the move for no less than 186min if it is a Chester service, or 176min if it is for Ellesmere Port. All have frequent stops. The distance covered is 71.5 miles for the Chester services, at an average speed of 23mph.

The only train crew depot is at Birkenhead Central where crew changes take place. This is served directly by services

on the line to Hooton only, but all trains will pass there at some stage in their diagrams.

There are, however, down sides. Such a cleverly put together service has to be planned and operated as one; there is little scope for offering a 15min service on one leg and a 20min service elsewhere. This would also cause timing conflicts around the Liverpool loop. Likewise, train capacity becomes a constant; a three-car operation to West Kirby would not mix easily with a six-car operation to New Brighton. All services are operated by the Class 507/508 fleets, which are effectively homogeneous.

There is also the risk of exporting any operational shortcomings. A major delay suffered anywhere on the network will affect all the Wirral line services, rather than being localised. It is for this reason that a siding in the little-used bay at Hooton has recently been electrified, so that a disabled train can be moved out of the way and clear of the running lines. Finally, peak supplementation, to the extent that it is deemed necessary, creates its own problems. Not the least of these is how to insert additional trains into the timetable in such a way that keeps the gaps between successive services reasonably even. Ways of skip-stopping peak services on the line to Hooton to speed up services are being examined.

Similar service provision arrangements may be found elsewhere. Other cities may have some circular element in the service provision, such as the Kingston loop of South West Trains in London, or ScotRail's Hamilton loop in Glasgow, but Liverpool's city centre terminal loop is unique.

Case study on timetable efficiency 2: Midland Main Line

This shows how the integration of an operator's own service plan can be achieved, using Midland Main Line as an example. The Midland line has always been bedevilled by serving principal towns such as Leicester, Nottingham, Derby and Sheffield, but also gains worthwhile traffics at many other intermediate points. A secondary issue is that the Nottingham service has to be separated from that to Derby and Sheffield as it is on a different line. The problem is how to balance the provision of a fast service for the longer distances but at the same time to provide a worthwhile service for the rest.

The key is in the four-platformed station at Leicester, 99 miles from St Pancras. A stopping service leaves St Pancras on the hour, calling as shown, and arriving at Leicester 4min before the xx.25 departure from London which follows it nonstop. Cross-platform interchange can then take place, with the fast train running thence to Sheffield and the stopping service following it but to Nottingham. 30min later, a similar pattern of service is provided, but the fast service this time is to Nottingham and the stopping train to Derby (only). North of Derby, there are additional services provided by other TOCs. On the MML stopping service, Bedford is substituted for Luton. *(See table on right.)*

This approach offers a good spread of services to meet most needs, with the stopping service (provided by the new Midland Main Line Class 170/1 Turbostars) spending 8min at Leicester. Examination of the basic timetable will show a few shortcomings, and a journey from Luton to Long Eaton, for instance, would be rather tedious.

But timetables cannot be built around minority flows, other than incidentally. The season ticket holder between Tamworth and Wigan on the West Coast main line complained loudly when his service was retimed and made the journey impractical. That the service was ever provided at all was purely by chance and not by any deliberate action. Even though he provided worthwhile revenue, the maxim of the greatest good for the greatest number must guide the service providers. It is also the way to earn revenue.

To be fair to Midland Main Line, the service described is still in its infancy and there are, in any event, adjustments to the basic service to cater better for Loughborough, for instance. This station receives a call from a Nottingham HST service, but only on alternate hours. Timetables should never be regarded as sacrosanct for all time; passenger needs change and new opportunities present themselves. A test of any timetable is the ability of the stock rostered for it to cope with the numbers of customers presenting themselves.

Rolling Stock

Railway rolling stock was comprehensively renewed as a result of the 1955 Modernisation Plan; the last remnants from that era have perhaps a limited life left. The only exceptions are the humble 350hp 0-6-0 diesel shunters; these go back to 1952, but they were developed directly from a 1944 LMS/English Electric design. From an original fleet size of 1,192, their numbers today are about one third of that total. Fifteen years ago it was possible for a commentator to write 'no words of praise could rate too highly these tough and reliable machines', and few would disagree with that assessment now.

Until the delivery of the Class 67 125mph locomotives for EWS with their electric train heating (ETH) capability, there are no diesel locomotives suitable for passenger services from the modern era. The electric fleets include the Class 90s on the WCML and Class 91s on the ECML, and that is about it. The future again appears to lie in the multiple-unit.

Modern coaching stock has progressed to the extent that recent builds for long-distance work feature fully integral construction, air conditioning, power-operated external doors at the vehicle ends only and a body which will allow an element of tilt. At least some vehicles on a train must allow for wheelchair access.

London St Pancras	d	xx.00	xx.25		xx.30	xx.55	
Luton	d	xx.24					
Bedford	d				x1.06		
Wellingborough	d	xx.51			x1.28		
Kettering	d	x1.00			x1.28		
Market Harborough	d	x1.11			x1.39		
Leicester	a	x1.30	x1.34	<—	x2.00	x2.04	<—
Leicester	d	—>	x1.34	x1.38	—>	x2.04	x2.08
Loughborough	d			x1.51			x2.22
Beeston	d			x2.04			
Nottingham	d			x2.10		x2.36	
Long Eaton	d						x2.31
Derby	a		x1.59				x2.42
Derby	d		x2.00				
Chesterfield	d		x2.18				
Sheffield	a		x2.36				

Above;
Merseyrail Electrics No 507003 is at Hamilton Square on a service about to cross beneath the River Mersey and enter the loop on 2 May 1999. The Class 507 units were built for Liverpool; the later but similar Class 508s were imported from what is now South West Trains. *Author*

Seating is generally arranged on each side of a central gangway, on a 2+1 layout for First Class and 2+2 for Standard Class. First Class seating is nearly always arranged face to face, usually across a table, but Standard Class is frequently arranged in pairs, face to back. First Class also has a more generous seat pitch, giving more leg room. On a 23m Mk3 vehicle, the Open Standard class design was built with 72 seats, which has been increased usually to 76 seats with the face-to-back arrangement. First Class vehicles were built with 48 seats, which are generally retained. In both classes, the accommodation for luggage has sometimes been increased, and also wheelchair spaces provided; this has led to variations in the current seating capacities. However, based on the 76/48 seat ratios, the First Class passenger occupies 1.58 x the floor area of the Standard Class, which certainly justifies a sizeable fare surcharge.

For suburban work, modern vehicles have Tightlock couplings, two sets of double-sliding plug doors per vehicle side and, again, integral construction. Lavatories may or may not be provided. Seating is now down to 2+2 in First Class when offered, and 2+3 in Standard. It may be mentioned here that seat arrangements need to be taken in conjunction with the vehicle body widths; today, these range between 2.69m and 2.82m. For comparison, the maximum legal width of a bus is 2.5m, which is the same as that of the former 'narrow' Hastings diesel units.

Vehicle design is a compromise between the provision of seating, standing space, and allowing for access. More doors and wider doors mean faster access and egress, and reduced station stop times. But they also mean fewer seats. Generally, it has become the accepted wisdom that on the so-called outer suburban services, proportionally more seating is required than on the inner services. On the latter, journey times are less and the distances travelled shorter. There are more likely to be some very short-distance journeys such as Charing Cross to Waterloo on Connex South Eastern, for people wanting access to South West Trains services from the main line station.

Suburban services are common to the major cities. Those with the good fortune of Birmingham, Manchester and Glasgow to have cross-city lines have exploited them to produce services such as Lichfield Trent Valley-Birmingham New Street-Redditch, Buxton-Manchester Piccadilly-Blackpool North, and Motherwell-Glasgow Central-Dalmuir. Only some of these will be electrified. If the service is provided by that 1980s aberration, the four-wheeled Pacer units, their ride quality and generally basic interiors do not encourage the making of long journeys.

Maintenance and Servicing

Trains have to be looked after, both technically in the sense of maintenance work from time to time and in terms of the passenger accommodation. North Pole International, used by Eurostar trains, is not perhaps typical, but it gives an idea of what is required.

North Pole, named after a nearby public house, is the main facility where service examinations, heavy maintenance and repair work are undertaken on the 400m-long trains.

From arrival at the site in one of the four reception sidings, the trains can proceed through the carriage washer or on the avoiding line and then to the lavatory discharge facility. This is required where

there are retention toilets in the rail vehicles.

The train then reverses into the service shed. There are six service roads, all raised, and each taking a complete 400m 20-vehicle Eurostar train. A central pit runs the complete length of the roads, allowing access to the underside of the trains. All roads are equipped with water, electricity, compressed air and overhead cranage.

The train can then proceed to stabling sidings or the departure road. An alternative is the maintenance workshop. Here, there are four service roads, two of which are equipped with retractable catenary. These accommodate half-sets of Eurostars. Each road has moveable access steps. Like the service shed, all roads are equipped with services, but Road 4 also has a simultaneous lift. This facility can lift a complete half-set of a Eurostar Class 373 train, approximately 200m in length. By using this facility, all 24 wheelsets can be exchanged.

Also available is the wheel lathe. This is capable of turning both wheels of both axles at the same time and can be adapted to the dimensions of most rail vehicles. It can also machine locomotive wheelsets. The bogie drop can exchange rapidly the individual wheelsets or complete bogies. There are also heavy lifting facilities.

Such facilities are considerably in excess of those available to the average TOC. They were built new for the Eurostar trains and

Above left:
External cleaning is achieved by taking trains through the depot carriage washer; this is the about-to-be-commissioned unit at Slade Green depot on 27 March 1992. Its capability extends to body sides, skirts and roofs; it is fully reversible in the sense that a train can approach from either end, and it is capable of automatic control. *Author*

Above right:
This is a double-headed ground wheel lathe, which can reprofile simultaneously all four wheels on a bogie. It removes any flats or other irregularities which accumulate on wheels in daily use. Made by Hegenschiedt, this installation is at Slade Green, where it was photographed on 27 March 1992 giving attention to an EPB vehicle. The Networkers were yet to arrive. *Author*

are securely fenced. This is in part due to the requirements of HM Customs. The entire site is about 3km in length, and bicycles — the decidedly low-tech but none the less effective solution — are provided for internal staff transport.

'If we (EWS) have any future at all, it will come from productivity, tight control of costs, competitive pricing and a strong service orientation.' Ed Burkhardt, Chairman & Chief Executive of EWS, 1996.

The Block Train

The block train was essentially a creation of the 1960s when the costs of the traditional wagonload traffic came under increasing scrutiny. The time taken in tripping wagons to marshalling yards, making them up into trains and distributing them again was not resulting in anything like sufficient wagon utilisation. Not only were unit costs high, but transit times were unimpressive, especially in the context of a growing road network. In 1962 the average time between loading a wagon and the subsequent loading was 11.9 working days, the average transit time was between 1.5 and two days, and the average journey length 67 miles.

The basic idea was outlined in *The Reshaping of British Railways*, also known as the (first) Beeching Report. It is here quoted verbatim to give a flavour of the era in which the concept was born.

'The description 'Liner Train' (later Freightliners) is applied to a conception of transport based upon joint use of road and rail for door-to-door transport of containerised merchandise, with special purpose, through-running, scheduled trains providing the trunk haul. It is envisaged as the future method of handling those flows of

6.

Freight Train Operation

traffic which are composed of consignments too small in themselves to make trainloads, but which aggregate heavy regular flows sufficient to support one or more trains per day.

'The advantages of the Railway are in the disciplined, safe, rapid movement of large tonnages at low cost. These advantages have generally been outweighed, firstly by the slow discharge of wagons, and secondly by the delays and damage inherent in collecting wagons in marshalling yards. The idea underlying the Liner Train is to by-pass both these obstacles to speed and economy. The expensive chassis of the wagon will no longer be marshalled, or be detained while goods are handled. Terminal delays will affect only the body.

'The Liner Train then is a train of chassis which will remain continuously coupled. It will cater for the longer distance traffics and will run to a strict timetable calling for high

Right:
The once very common, but now seen a little less, combination of a Class 56 and a train of merry-go-round hopper wagons. These have the extended sides, allowing them to carry more. No 56053 heads east through Pelaw, Tyne & Wear, on 18 March 1998.
Author

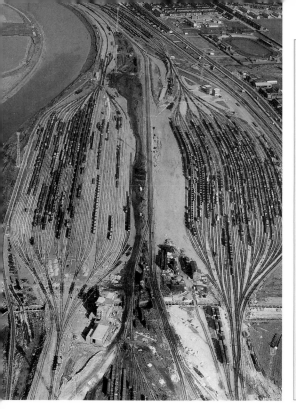

Left:
This aerial view of Tees Marshalling Yard was taken in October 1962, but the yard did not open formally until 21 May 1963. This view shows clearly both the size of these yards, and the method of operation by pushing wagons over a hump (bottom left, also top right) and letting them roll under gravity into one of the sorting sidings.
BR/Author's collection

utilisation of the stock. It will carry containers and, when fully loaded, it will have a gross load of 680 tons and a payload of 360 tons. The speed will be a maximum of 75 and an average of 50 miles an hour.

'By their combination of speed, reliability in all weathers, freedom from damage and pilferage, and convenience of service, Liner Trains will surpass anything known by rail or road.'

The containers, it might be added, would all be of the then new international standard of 8ft x 8ft. The lengths were to be 10ft, 20ft and 27ft, the last to be 30ft 'when road regulations permit'. Half the traffic, estimated to be 39m tons per year, was for distances of less than 150 miles.

Wagonload traffic survived for a time, and the concept was rethought, but was finally discontinued at the beginning of the 1990s. Or so it then seemed. Trainload operation nowadays requires a load of 500 tonnes or thereabouts as a minimum. What if the volume is less, but still potentially profitable? EWS now operates its 'Enterprise' services in which wagons can be tripped from a terminal to a hub, where they are then picked up by a long-distance freight. A similar trip movement can take place at the receiving end of the transit.

There may also be a limited opportunity for remarshalling the long-distance freight to provide an increased range of destinations. The trick here is to make sure that journey times do not suffer, and that shunting, tripping and remarshalling costs do not have the same disastrous effects about which the late Lord Beeching complained in 1963. There is, however, a vast range of traffic which does not move in trainload quantities, and the indications are that the service is going well.

Modern Freight

After a postwar high of 294m tonnes lifted (or forwarded) in 1953, rail freight volumes fell steadily to 154m tonnes in 1980 and dropped to 97m tonnes in 1994/5. Since then, there has certainly been some recovery. The measurement of tonne-km, which takes account also of distance, showed a similar decline on a historical basis.

On those figures, rail freight today is doing little more than a third of the business of nearly half a century ago. Absolute carryings by rail have declined in a growing market.

But matters are changing. The core freight business of rail over the years has been the large-scale bulk movements of coal, metals, aggregates, petroleum and a few other products such as chemicals and automotive products. This has been supplemented by the non-bulk market, represented by intermodal movements (Freightliner in particular) and international services. Other important traffics include the Royal Mail services and the EWS 'Enterprise' wagonload operation.

Prospects, by Sector
Coal

The most precipitate decline in rail carryings occurred in the carriage of coal and coal products. This was partly due to the 'dash for gas' to fuel the power stations, but the tonnage carried by road hauliers changed little.

On the other hand, a significant proportion of imported coal movements are handled by rail, for instance Avonmouth to Didcot and Liverpool to Fidlers Ferry. The result is that the average length of haul has increased, partly due to the imported coal but also to the concentration of both coal production and electricity generation on fewer sites. Coal movements remain rail's largest freight activity but Railtrack, in its Network Management Statement for 1999, is not expecting any future growth.

Iron and Steel

Rail did well during the 1980s, but during the 1990s carryings by all modes have fallen, and there has been a continuing small erosion of rail's market share.

British Steel's demand for trainload freight movements arises at three stages:

- Imported iron ore and coking coal, and some limestone.
- Bulk steel semi-finished products.
- Finished products to inland break-bulk sites, to final consumers or to ports for export.

Substantial gains are anticipated here by Railtrack from the integration of manufacturing operations and more intra-European movements. These are thought to be worth 17% pa over the next five years.

Right:
The box van grew in length over the years, but still retained its four-wheeled chassis. The 12-ton 18cwt van can carry a 22-ton payload. The posing of the van with the doors wide open helps demonstrate its capacity. *Author's collection*

Left:
Perhaps a more effective way of loading a wagon than doors in a box van is to enable the whole of the body to be slid back, as in this bogie CargoWaggon pictured in Docklands on 5 October 1994.
Peter Ashton

Below left:
Intermodal vehicles have been around for a long time, though they were not called that when the RoadRailer was first unveiled in 1960. This picture shows the Pressed Steel vehicle, 'which combines the flexibility and convenience of road movement, for collection and delivery of freight, with the speed and economy of railways for the trunk haul'. Isn't it small?
BR/Author's collection

Oil and Petroleum

There has been a steady decline in rail traffic, matched by a steady growth in road traffic, so that the rail's share is now less than a quarter. In petroleum, the demand for rail freight has fallen despite an increase in the output from UK refineries. The cause appears to be linked to changes in the organisation of production and distribution of oil products. Railtrack forecasts a 12% pa growth over the next five years.

Construction

There was a small net increase in rail traffic volumes between the early 1980s and the mid-1990s. Rail construction traffic, much of which is aggregates, has broadly followed the trends in the industry. Here, activity is closely related to the state of the national economy. Growth anticipated by Railtrack amounts to a 'safe' 10% pa.

Rail movement volumes of other types of traffic, including unitised and international traffic, declined between the early 1980s and early 1990s. Recently, traffic of this kind has increased strongly, especially since the opening of freight services through the Channel Tunnel. Here, Railtrack clearly sees that major advances can be made. From an admittedly limited base, the company anticipates 41% annual growth in the international freight market for rail over the five year period, and domestic intermodal at 15% pa.

SWOT Analysis

Strengths

Rail has high fixed costs, but relatively low variable or distance-related costs; rail also has advantages at higher demand levels due to the size of wagons and the capacity of a train. High volumes and/or longer distances are where rail scores.

Mine (or ship's side) to power station coal has no terminal transfer problems, and no associated time or cost related penalties. Such traffics will always be well suited to rail.

Weaknesses

The penalty of collection and/or delivery by road when necessary for non-bulk traffic, coupled with the quality of service differentials, suggest that the break-even distance before rail becomes truly competitive can be as high as 450 miles. Little domestic traffic travels such a distance.

Opportunities

The accessibility of rail might be improved by an expansion in the numbers of private sidings, which in turn could encourage the relocation of manufacturing industry. The non-bulk market is relatively price-insensitive. Rail could make substantial inroads if it could guarantee levels of service similar to those offered by road hauliers in terms of punctuality, reliability and flexibility.

Threats

Larger articulated road vehicles have replaced smaller rigid ones in recent years. Over 60% of road tonne-km are carried in artics which are over 33 tonnes gross weight. Further liberalisation of hgv weights might take place. Operating costs have declined by 3-4% per annum on average over a 10-year period.

Freight Operating Companies

English, Welsh & Scottish Railway is owned by a consortium led by Wisconsin Central Transportation Corp of the USA. The company acquired the former Rail Express Systems, Trainload Freight and Railfreight Distribution businesses from the British Railways Board between 1995 and 1997.

EWS acquired a variety of locomotive types. Those of Classes 66/67 are presently under construction for EWS. Apart from around 250 diesel shunters, EWS owns the whole of the Class 56, 58 and 60 heavy-haul fleets, totalling 271 locomotives. Of electric locomotives, the company owns 25 of the Class 90s and 14 of the Class 86s. Many of the electric locomotives were previously part of the Rail Express Systems' fleet. From the RfD stable came the 30 Class 92s for international services.

A large fleet of earlier locomotives is becoming surplus as the Class 66s (250 locomotives) and Class 67s (30 locomotives) are delivered.

EWS also owns 19,000 wagons, operating from 40 depots and 340 sidings and terminals. It runs more than 1,000 trains per day and lifts over 90m tonnes of freight by rail every year. As well as the locomotives on order, there are 2,500 new wagons under construction.

EWS is the largest of the freight-operating companies, whose operations extend into continental Europe as well as within Britain, for both conventional wagon and intermodal traffic, either in trainload or in unit/wagon-load quantities.

Freightliner Ltd was sold to a management buyout team in May 1996. The company is an intermodal operator which provides rail haulage and associated road movements for containerised freight within the UK. Most movements are between inland locations and seaports, forming the first or last leg of a deep-sea business. There is also some domestic freight.

The company has 49 diesel locomotives, including the Class 57s which are being rebuilt from the Class 47 fleet with new General Motors 2,500hp engines. Freightliner also has 40 ac electric locomotives, 10 of which are Class 90s and 30 of the older BR/English Electric Class 86 machines.

Freightliner operates about 90 trains in a British network which includes approximately 110 single flows carrying over 0.5 million containers a year. There are port terminals at Felixstowe, Southampton Maritime, Tilbury, Purfleet, Isle of Grain (Thamesport) and Seaforth, and 13 others inland.

DRS provides rail haulage, principally for its parent company British Nuclear Fuels Ltd. The traffic consists of nuclear products.

Locomotives

The freight locomotive needs considerable adhesive weight, which is a function of that which is carried by the driving wheels. The greater the adhesive weight, the greater the power which can be applied to the driving wheels before they start to slip. Adhesion is also a function of rail conditions, which are affected particularly by the weather. Slippery rails mean lower adhesion rates.

For diesel locomotives, the power output developed by the engine is used principally for traction, though some will be used for other equipment. The traction power drives a generator and the electric current produced is fed to the traction motors. Thus a larger diesel engine equals more power to the generator, leading to more electric current and more power at the wheel/rail interface. This is required to move the locomotive and its train away from a standing position. To avoid overheating the electrical equipment, power must be reduced as the train gathers speed. Power may be sustained at the level which the traction motors can absorb on a continuous basis.

Electric transmission is now standard throughout all classes of locomotive.

For electric locomotives, the power available from the supply over short periods is effectively unlimited. This allows electric traction to accelerate more quickly than diesel, and hence offers some performance benefits.

With any form of traction, the brake power must be sufficient to stop the load being hauled within the signalling distance.

Rolling Stock

Conventional wagons may be divided into the following generic types:

- Open wagons, maybe with removable covers; includes hopper wagons. Used for bulk solids such as coal, iron ore, sand, granite, limestone and scrap. Loaded from above with bulk loaders or by grab cranes. Bottom or side discharge doors, or no doors and unloaded by grab.
- Tank wagons. Used for the carriage of liquids, gases, grain, ash and powders. Loading and unloading usually by pipeline connection, either with a storage tank or a road vehicle. With powders such as cement, a pressurised discharge is often necessary.
- Vans and covered wagons. Used for general merchandise, often palletised and loaded through side doors or, occasionally, curtains. Insulated and

refrigerated versions may be available.
- Flat wagons. Various forms and used for bulky items, especially steel products. Stanchions may be raised to help secure loads in transit.
- Automotive wagons, may have limited or total side protection. The limits of the British loading gauge make double-stacking of cars difficult; this was first achieved satisfactorily in a four-section articulated carrier. Larger road vehicles must use flat wagons, which may include superannuated coaching stock with bodies removed. Loading and unloading is through ends of wagons, thus requiring placement against end dock or similar.
- Other specialised wagons include well wagons for large loads, those for nuclear flask traffic, and service vehicles for use on railway business. These latter include cranes and snowploughs as well as those for ballast and similar commodities.

Intermodal wagon fleets reflect the technology concerned. The basic flat wagons for containers as used by Freightliners will accommodate various combinations of container length which together total 60ft. These wagons use bar coupling and run in multiples of complete rakes. This obviates the cost of buffing gear and the space which it takes up on all but the end wagons. Containers are secured to the wagon by twistlocks or spigots located on the vehicle.

Other wagon varieties offer various means of accommodating additional height. This includes well wagons, in which the central area between the bogies is lowered, but the area above the bogies remains unused and represents wasted space. There are also various designs which provide a pocket for the wheels of a road trailer, or incorporate a swinging portion which enables a road trailer to be loaded or unloaded without the use of cranage. All are, however, somewhat limited by the restrictions of the British loading gauge.

While many wagons may be owned by the operating companies and the rates for the carriage of a trader's goods include an element for the use of the wagon, private wagon companies have long been extant in Britain. This has always been the case for some of the more specialist wagons, as opposed to the common opens or vans. This class of wagon is typified by the tank, the

nature of loads such as petroleum products not favouring a common-user approach. In theory, private ownership favours wagons returning empty to origin rather than finding other revenue-earning work in the vicinity.

The biggest change has taken place with the more mundane wagons, whether they be those for roadstone, fertilizers, cement, cars or general merchandise. Coupled with the renewal of the wagon fleets, the carrying capacity of the wagons themselves has also risen. Even 30 years ago, at the end of steam traction, the average wagon on British Railways could carry no more than 16 tons.

Terminals

Freight terminals and the facilities to be provided depend very much on the commodity to be carried if a bulk traffic, and the type of wagon or intermodal vehicle used otherwise. Unlike passengers, freight will not load or unload itself. This statement of the obvious is nevertheless one of the reasons why freight terminal provision and the equipment needed may represent considerable expense, both in its installation and in its operation.

The terminal itself may be a private siding, as in the sense of a colliery which dispatches coal to power stations. Other private sidings may be connected to warehouses or manufacturing plants. Thus, Ford has a large installation at Dagenham.

This enables rail freight services direct access to the points of dispatch or receipt. The best possible situation for rail is where no other form of transport is used, other perhaps than conveyor belts. Colliery to power station coal is in this category, as it removes the need for separate road movements and, from the customer's point of view, the associated costs.

Common-user terminals are open, in the sense that they serve more than one customer. They may include warehousing linked to rail, and intermodal transfer facilities such as the road/rail operations at Daventry. Typically, these are run by Freight Operating Companies or third-party logistics providers. The requirements and the extent for onward movements will also vary. These terminals have their own implications for the traffic effects on local roads and for environmental matters generally.

Lineside hardstanding is the most basic of provisions. Railtrack will permit direct loading or unloading of trains on running lines, provided the existing timetable can

accommodate such movements. By definition, this will be a relatively rare occurrence. It is likely to be acceptable only for short-term or seasonal flows of traffic on secondary and lightly used routes.

In busier areas, an alternative is the construction of a temporary private siding. This is particularly relevant to the construction industry, where the project is completed and the teams move on. Thus, a single siding was constructed next to the up main line at Normanton, adjacent to what was to become the M62.

There is also the station platform. This may be used to a limited extent for parcels traffic and similar, provided that platform occupation requirements are consistent with other uses by passenger train operators and that road/rail transfer can be accomplished safely.

The scale of the terminal will need to reflect the maximum length of train using it. Long trains may be economical in provision terms, but they do have implications for the tonnages and/or volumes to be handled.

The time taken to load and/or unload is another factor in determining how long the terminal will be occupied.

Also, wagon capacity is only part of the equation. The payload of a wagon may be limited by the volume of the goods carried if they are essentially of a low-density nature, rather than weight. It is just not possible to get any more in.

Neither should it be assumed that a wagon can always be filled; a high-density load may reach the weight carrying capacity of a simple box-type wagon before it is full in terms of it being about to overflow. Put another way, the axle-load (or other) limits of the wagon will be reached before it is full.

Train length depends on the weight or length restrictions on the journey made, as well as the characteristics of the terminal at the other end of the journey. Ideally, trains are dealt with as a single unit, but practical considerations often require their subdivision within a terminal. Relevant matters here include siding length and the dimensions of the terminal site, particularly length.

Another element concerns the frequency of services; a terminal which may need to deal with four long trains simultaneously is of necessity a much larger operation than a terminal with one train on alternate days. This is in no sense intended to marginalise the latter. Success in these areas lies more with matching usage and capacity, and low

usage levels are of little consequence if the associated costs are low also.

Freight traffic may be a short-term or a longer term requirement. For example, aggregates will probably be produced at a quarry until such time as the quarry itself is exhausted. Terminal locations which are more likely to be firmly based include those at ports, oil refineries and steelworks. A word of warning, though, is that although the facility may remain, future uncritical commitment of traffic to rail should never be assumed.

Handling Equipment
There has to be a means of aligning the terminal equipment hardware with the wagons; either the hardware can move along the line of wagons as with a Freightliner crane or a mobile grab on pneumatic tyres, or the train itself can be drawn through some fixed equipment, as used when loading merry-go-round wagons at a colliery.

The classic colliery-to-power station merry-go-round movement will see a freight locomotive pull a train of (say) 36 hoppers slowly beneath an overhead bunker at the colliery for loading, and depart directly to the power station. Here, it takes the wagons over the discharging pits from which the coal is removed by conveyor belt. The bottom doors are opened by a cam engaging the door controls as each wagon reaches the pits, and another shuts them as it leaves. The speed is a constant 0.5mph, so the

unloading takes about 30min. Given the construction of a terminal loop as at Didcot, Eggborough and Drax power stations, there is no need for the train to come to a halt.

Loading or unloading of bulk products may be possible using mobile equipment, which itself can be moved by road between terminals as required. This might include mobile cranes for use with box wagons, tankers for pumping liquids or powders to and from rail tank wagons, and trucks with integral grab cranes. A variation, little used as yet, is to build transfer equipment into the train itself. An example is the Redland Self-Discharging Train for aggregates.

Intermodal transfer equipment is required for containers, swap-bodies and piggyback trailers. For these, the gantry crane is one solution, as used in many Freightliner depots, and the other is the front-loading reachstacker unit. Specialist systems such as RoadRailer may use equally specialised equipment.

Other equipment of more general use includes fork lift trucks, which may be used to load or unload a railway van directly and transfer the contents to a warehouse or to road vehicles.

Fixed terminal equipment requires the use of locomotive power and is likely to be capital intensive.

Power may be provided by the train locomotive, but this tends to be costly if the locomotive is detained on site for any length of time. An alternative is shunting power retained for this purpose. Shunting power can be used also to reposition wagons for static loading or unloading; the need for this will be to some extent determined by the scale of the facility but also by the nature of the unloading equipment.

Within the terminal, site facilities such as stacking of goods or containers, or warehousing, will take up space. If specialised functions such as customs clearance at a large terminal are to be undertaken, there will be additional requirements.

Management Control Systems

The development of the computerised Total Operations Processing System (TOPS) was begun in 1963 by the US Southern Pacific Railroad. The system was purchased by the British Railways Board in 1971, when there were three principal expectations. These were:

- TOPS would considerably improve the efficiency of freight movement and rolling stock utilisation.
- It would give staff and customers current information on any consignment on request.
- Operating, maintenance and planning departments would be provided with accurate up-to-date information on any and every aspect of the freight business.

Initially, the purpose was very much freight oriented. Today, it contains details of every vehicle which is authorised to operate over the National Railways system, together with the various locations. From the initial business case outlined above developed the control and maintenance of passenger and parcels rolling stock and locomotives. Up until the time of the introduction of TOPS, there was no system to identify the individual location of freight vehicles on the network.

Each freight vehicle is allocated a three-letter code from which can be identified the type of rolling stock and the method of braking. For wagons, the first letter is to divide the stock into broad categories, thus V is for van, M for mineral, B for bogie bolster and so on. The second letter subdivides each category. The third letter denotes the braking system, A being for air brakes and V for vacuum. Thus BBA is a bogie steel wagon, 50ft long, with air brakes.

In addition, freight vehicles have codes to identify their current status — loaded or empty, available for traffic or stopped for repair, the commodity represented by the load, details of any dangerous goods, and any movement restrictions.

In a similar fashion for coaching stock, but with a four-part code, the first two letters denote the layout and AA is a gangwayed corridor vehicle and AB also has a brake. The number gives the class of accommodation (3 being a composite) and the last letter the build of coach. G is Mk3 or Mk3a, and J denotes Mk4. As an example, AD1F is a gangwayed open vehicle with 2+1 seating, first class, and of the Mk2f build.

Identification codes are also applied to passenger vehicles and locomotives identifying the operating status, maintenance requirements or work done, or any special characteristics.

For TOPS purposes, all vehicles have a number unique to themselves. Locomotives also have a two-digit class number which precedes that of the individual serial number. Thus No 91023 is No 23 of Class 91. The same system is applied to multiple-units, both electric and diesel; the vehicle number is separate and in addition to the set number. The table (below) gives the main groups into which locomotives and rolling stock are divided.

In very general terms, diesel locomotives increase in power as the classification number rises. In all the principal class groups, the higher numbers now reflect the more recent builds. Preserved diesel and electric locomotives licensed to run on Railtrack carry either their original numbers or are included in Class 89.

A five-figure reference number identifies the location of every station, siding, depot and workshop.

Information on every vehicle movement is advised to the Area Freight Centre (TOPS office) by a nominated person responsible for each location. From this the computer generates up-to-date information and a train list for every train service. The list contains the train identification or working timetable number, locomotive number, wagon numbers, codes and position in train, details of any dangerous goods together with their classification and reporting requirements in the event of any emergency. Details of maximum load, brake force, route availability and length are calculated for each wagon and totalled for the train, including the locomotive. This information must be checked and validated by the person responsible for train preparation before being handed to the driver.

Above right:
A train of four-wheeled Traffic Services Ltd tank wagons for international traffic is propelled towards the photographer, location and date unknown.
Author's collection

Right:
100-ton tank wagons discharge fuel oil at the Haydock Oil Terminal for Shell.
Author's collection

TOPS classification of locomotives and multiple-units

01-70	diesel locomotives
71-80	dc electric locomotives or dual system dc/diesel locomotives
81-99	ac electric locomotives or dual system ac/dc locomotives
101-199	diesel multiple-units
201-299	diesel-electric multiple-units
301-399	ac electric multiple-units or dual system ac/dc units*
401-599	dc electric multiple-units (includes unpowered sets)
901-949	service units, diesel or electric

* includes Eurostar Class 373 units of up to four electrification systems.

Many enquiries are available to assist in the daily operation of services, thus ensuring the most efficient use of resources. In addition to the control of locomotive and vehicle maintenance activities referred to earlier, the system can provide summary information on the loading and punctuality of individual services, the employment of vehicle pools, transit times and other statistics. It also provides information for the automatic billing of customers.

The system is also interfaced with automatic train running information systems throughout the country so that up-to-date information is available to anyone with an enquiry terminal.

English, Welsh & Scottish Railways' investment programme includes a Transportation Control System for its Customer Delivery Centre at Doncaster. This is designed to replace the TOPS system and streamline the business process from order to invoice. What effect this will have on the system-wide operation of TOPS in the new millennium is as yet unclear.

Royal Mail

The Post Office's Royal Mail business makes considerable use of the railway, with the Railnet project revolutionising the way in which mail is handled by rail.

The new train plan is based wholly on 65 dedicated Royal Mail trains. Of these, 18 are Travelling Post Offices in which loose bags are opened and sorted on the train, but all also carry the new York mail containers. Containerisation of letter mail enables the loading and unloading of trains to be that much faster.

A fleet of 16 x Class 325 four-car units owned by Royal Mail forms 22 of the trains. The Class 325s may be used on ac or dc electrified lines, but are used principally between the new Princess Royal Distribution Centre (PRDC) at Wembley and Glasgow (via West Coast), Edinburgh (via East Coast), Norwich and Tonbridge. They may be hauled over non-electrified lines.

The remaining 25 trains are formed of locomotive and vans. A fleet of MkI vans has been adapted with roller shutter doors and to carry York containers. A new vehicle has been introduced in the form of 46 Propelling Control Vehicles (PCV). The PCVs are converted from Class 307 EMUs with retained driving cab and corridor connection. They are used for short-distance reversing movements at speeds up to 40mph. The second driver who is in the PCV communicates with the locomotive driver on power requirements and has control over the train braking. PCVs are permitted to run at 100mph when hauled. Their main use is for WCML non-EMU trains for reversal at PRDC and on GWML trains which need to reverse at Kensal Green.

Mail is no longer carried on ordinary passenger services. All London mail traffic used the new Princess Royal Distribution Centre at Wembley from September 1996, and a series of other dedicated railheads. These feature platforms 250mm higher than normal at 1.225m above the rail head. This eases the roll on and roll off of the York containers. It is one reason for the shutter doors on the vans, as conventional swing doors will foul the platform. The other is to maximise the space available for movement on any platform.

PRDC features seven platforms as well as road vehicle accommodation and the sorting hall. The site was chosen for its proximity to the M1 and M40 as well as the national rail network in general and the WCML in particular. Each platform is 260m in length and can thus take 12-car trains. Each is signalled for multi-train usage. All trains can use any platform. They are equipped for 25kV throughout, and diesel fume extractors are fitted.

The relationship of PRDC with the rest of the rail network is shown in Fig 6.1:

Occasionally, ordinary passenger stations are used as opposed to the specially constructed Railnet premises at Low Fell (Newcastle), Tonbridge, Doncaster and elsewhere. Royal Mail trains must be confined to the nominated platform, as the York container handling equipment cannot easily be moved elsewhere.

The train plan is arranged in three distinct waves:

- 14.00-15.00 early afternoon is for second class
- 19.00-20.00 mid-evening from the early afternoon collections, the First Class relief
- 22.00-23.00 overnight network, including TPOs, rest of the First Class collections, the First Class final.

Long-distance rail services may cater for more than one postal wave at different points of their journeys. But mail by rail is

Princess Royal Distribution Centre and links to railway network.

Right:
A Cartic four-section articulated car carrier brings up the rear of an automotive freight, seen here leaving Longbridge on 22 October 1997. The way in which the design tries to maximise the headroom available within the restricted loading gauge is apparent. *Author*

essentially a night-time operation, and time critical. With last postal collections at around 19.00, the mail has to be concentrated at the dedicated railheads and dispatched by 22.00. To ensure First Class deliveries from 07.00 onwards, the mail must have reached the inward rail centres by 03.00.

The emphasis is on point-to-point speeds and short stop times at intermediate points to reduce the overall journey times. Many trains connect with each other, either to combine or to transfer containers between trains, and all connect with Royal Mail road services.

Royal Mail, the Customer View

Unreliability can have a cumulative effect; consistency of operational performance is essential. The Royal Mail's customers are

unforgiving if the mail fails to arrive when it should, and time margins are very tight. Thus, if 1S09 20.05 Cardiff to Shieldmuir (Glasgow) TPO is 15min late, the mail on it misses the first morning deliveries outside the immediate Edinburgh and Glasgow areas. Royal Mail's contract requires a performance level of 95% of trains on time or within 10min of time, and this is measured at all calling points on the journey.

This has not been achieved, with shortfalls of around 3% on a rolling annual average basis. The delays are caused equally by Railtrack (where track circuit failures are the single biggest problem) and by the operator EWS.

Key issues for Royal Mail include consistent underperformance. Why do the final train movements perform worst? Do those in the railway control offices really understand what is at stake? The worst performing service achieves only 81% punctuality.

Second, Royal Mail needs the same service quality, every day, every week. Night-time engineering possessions can be very bad news. Punctuality is not an optional extra; connections between trains also have to be made.

On timetabling, Royal Mail would like to see complete stability where it is content, and instant reaction when the need changes. Naturally, this is acknowledged to be unrealistic, but a legalistic and bureaucratic process, which puts timetables to bed a year in advance of their introduction, is not sufficiently responsive to customer needs.

And when matters do go wrong in day-to-day operational terms, Royal Mail needs to know at the earliest opportunity so that it can replan resource deployment as far as possible.

Rail is not a cheap option for Royal Mail; the key is the service which can be offered. The railway is most competitive in the 100-250-mile distances for First Class traffic, where it can provide the fastest point-to-point times. (For second class, rail is used for distances above 150 miles.) There is scope for more rail use. New rolling stock will be needed for the locomotive-hauled services (at a considerable capital outlay), and this might be designed to run at maximum line speed and cut journey times. This could enable rail to carry First Class traffic for (say) 300-mile distances, provided track maintenance requirements do not become an insuperable problem. Rail could also be used at weekends if service consistency could be achieved.

Rail has much more potential for Royal Mail if, but only if, high service performance levels can be attained regularly.

TruckTrain

There are always new ideas, and the German CargoSprinter suggested that there were opportunities for a freight operation based more on the passenger multiple-unit principle. This indeed has been the approach of Royal Mail.

The TruckTrain concept is a high-powered diesel modular multiple-unit train, typically consisting of between two and five cars and

with payloads of up to 70 tonnes or 1,400 cubic metres per car. The vehicle concept is capable of being built either for direct loading with pallets or trolleys for plant-to-plant operation, or to carry ISO containers or swap-bodies of up to 48ft long and 9ft 6in high, and with a maximum gross container mass of 40 tonnes.

The freight market being addressed is the high value, time and quality sensitive transits for the food chain, retail, manufacturing and small lot logistics. Operating costs of TruckTrain have been estimated by its promoters as being between 30% and 80% of conventional wagonload or similar services.

New ideas are always welcome. If the technical idea is developed satisfactorily, there must be concern as to whether the railway could cope physically with more small volume individual transits which consume line capacity.

The Importance of Freight

The near doubling of domestic non-bulk and international traffics is dependent critically on price reductions and on significant improvements in service quality. Cost reductions would reduce the journey lengths over which rail is competitive with road for intermodal traffics by perhaps 100 miles. Road competition will not go away.

Finally, it is perhaps of interest to note the place which freight has had in railway fortunes. The earliest railways were built for the carriage of goods and little else. Freight was the foundation of the railway. This changed during the Victorian era, to the extent that they became mass passenger carriers as well.

In the period leading up to 1930, the Big Four railway companies gave evidence to the Railway Rates Tribunal as to the proportions of their total receipts which were derived from passenger traffic:

Passenger Receipts as a proportion of total receipts, c1929

Great Western Railway	43%
Southern Railway	72%
London, Midland & Scottish Railway	39%
London & North Eastern Railway	37%

Apart from the Southern, whose territory never included an industrial area of any real consequence, passenger traffic clearly took second place to freight. How has this has changed?

In the last year of the unified railway in 1993/4, the British Railways Board recorded the following statistics:

Passenger receipts	£2,165.8 million	77%
Parcels receipts	£77.9 million	3%
Freight receipts	£565.4 million	20%
Total	£2,809.1 million	100%

Even leaving aside the uncertain status of parcels traffic, which traditionally has been associated with passenger operations but is nowadays more freight related, the extent of the shift away from freight is deplorable. Freight traffic on the whole of the national system in 1993/4 accounted for a lower proportion of receipts than even the Southern Railway was achieving 60 years earlier.

The competitive environment and many other factors have changed, perhaps irrevocably. Nevertheless, this does perhaps lend additional credence to the aspirations of English, Welsh & Scottish Railway and of Freightliner. Both wish to increase their future traffic volumes hugely, to the extent that freight revenues might even begin to rival present passenger revenues.

The result would be a very different sort of railway.

Above:
This 100-ton gross wagon was built by the then Charles Roberts of Wakefield for sea-worked gravel traffic for Marinex. *Author's collection*

Below:
Private sidings and the routes to them need not involve excessive amounts or complexities of infrastructure. This is part of the Silvertown tramway in East London in 1979; the line has now been lifted and turned into a cycle track. *Author*

'A normal express into King's Cross would comprise 8, 10 or 12 coaches, but wartime strengthening habitually meant loads of 18 coaches. There was one case of a locomotive bringing in 1,300 passengers in a train of 26 vehicles.' R. T. Munns, *Milk Churns to Merry-Go-Round*, David & Charles, 1986.

Trains of 26 passenger vehicles are, let it be said, unlikely to form part of anybody's deliberate operational plan. The total length will be in the order of 550yd, and this will pose some difficulties for the signalling clearances. They will be an embarrassment at intermediate stations, with a need to draw up, perhaps twice. There is also the question of the adequacy of the motive power to move the train at all, but more specifically to accelerate away from stops and, in due course, to stop. It all consumes extra time.

On arrival at King's Cross, though, the problems intensify. The King's Cross station track layout is wedged between Euston Road to the south and Gasworks Tunnel to the north. This gives a maximum distance from buffer stops to tunnel mouth of about 480yd; the longest platform accommodates at best 12 coaches. The last three or four vehicles of

7.

Service Provision and Operational Planning

a 26-coach train would have remained in the tunnel.

This gives problems as follows:

• The time taken to detrain needed to allow for something like 700 passengers from

---

Below:
Such gloomy scenes do little for the railway. There is a disconnected track in the foreground. If you penetrate the site as far as can be seen in the photograph, you will indeed come across a line electrified on the third rail. The location is Silvertown, in November 1997. *Author*

This railway is operational.

DANGER OF ELECTROCUTION

Do not enter this site!

the rear of the train to walk through the corridors with all their luggage and out, probably, through a single door.

- The station throat (the area between the platform ends and the tunnel) would have been virtually paralysed, preventing most further movements.

- Removal of the empty stock would have required a pilot locomotive to enter Gasworks Tunnel from the north and couple to the train in total darkness, following which it would have to lift the stock up the not inconsiderable gradient to get it away to the carriage sidings. Even then, it might have been necessary to split the train before it could be stabled.

Although it was wartime, this was clearly an extreme case. However, it does perhaps demonstrate to the unwary some of the limitations associated with train planning.

Track Access

Railtrack, as the owner of the railway infrastructure, also controls the use of that infrastructure. A Train Operating Company wishing to run upon it needs to have an access agreement with Railtrack. These agreements cover the use of the track and signalling, electrification systems if appropriate, and support facilities.

The services provided by the different operators have varying status. The contract of a passenger franchisee with OPRAF will require him to run certain train services, as specified in the Passenger Service Requirement (PSR). It is essential, therefore,

that he has the corresponding access rights. This has, effectively, been achieved.

Most TOCs are running services additional to those to which they are committed by the PSR; in some cases these formed part of their franchise bid and have similar status.

Passenger operations, with negligible exceptions, need to run to a published timetable, with fixed departure and arrival times at the stations they serve. It does not, of course, rule out adjustments. These might reflect attempts by the TOC to match changing customer needs or for what might be termed internally generated railway reasons, such as to make best use of new rolling stock or to ensure connections with other services.

On the freight side, despite the growing importance of 'just-in-time'-type operations, timing is not often quite so constrained. The position of Royal Mail, though, has already been noted. Freight operators need greater flexibility and often a choice of routes; one option is to have a contract with Railtrack which gives rights to run a number of trains between two points within certain time bands, but no more specific than that. The term of a contract may need to be more variable, since flows can change.

Even in an apparently simple operation like merry-go-round, the reality is that power stations may want to vary the quality of the coal input from time to time. This means sourcing coal from more than one colliery and at short notice. The result was that Knottingley motive power depot on the

Yorkshire coalfield used to receive its train and train crew diagrams for the forthcoming week from the BR Leeds office on the previous Friday afternoon.

None of this prevents freight companies from entering into long-term specific access contracts, especially for flows which are unlikely to vary much in future. An example of this might be train paths between the West London line and the Channel Tunnel.

However, there are also the new passenger and freight operators, or the existing TOCs, who have commercial aspirations beyond what might be termed their home territories. Early manifestations have seen First North Western trains introducing services between northwest England and Euston, while Anglia Railways has made no secret of its wish to operate services from Ipswich to both Basingstoke and to Watford Junction, or beyond to Northampton. There would also be a Watford Junction to Basingstoke service. Another Anglia proposal is to run between Waterloo and Southampton Docks, with a spur operation from Eastleigh to Romsey.

The key infrastructure element for Anglia is the busy North London line between Stratford and the Willesden area, thence either to the West Coast main line or to the South Western main line via Feltham and Chertsey.

It is not difficult to see some practical difficulties in linking up timetable paths on a series of four separate railways, all busy. This is far from saying that it cannot be done, but the contractual rights of others also have to be taken into account. From the point of view of the infrastructure owner, the more access agreements which it can make, the more revenue the company earns. There is thus every incentive to accommodate the wishes of operators to run additional services.

Suitable rolling stock also has to be obtained. An Ipswich-Northampton service could use ac electric traction, but to Basingstoke the electrification systems are a mixture of ac overhead, dc third rail and none at all. For the latter, diesel units are the only short-term answer and would be needed for all services if they were to be operated as an Ipswich-Northampton-Basingstoke-Ipswich diagram. Proposals of this nature do have some competitive implications for the well-being of the existing franchises, and both OPRAF and ORR have an interest.

Train Frequencies

There are three basic choices in passenger service planning:

• run services at specific and perhaps irregular times to meet known, anticipated or researched demands;
• tailor frequencies to a standard 20min, 30min, 60min, or whatever; or
• operate at times designed largely around good stock utilisation.

The specific operations option does have its attractions. There is no point in trying to pick up factory workers if the train departs 5min before the end of a shift, and the next is 55min later. The same applies to schools.

However, the large numbers of potential customers along a line of route, all with different constraints, tend to make this approach impractical. More relevant is the case of business or commuter trips to a major centre. A service arriving at the rail terminus at around 08.30 is likely to suit many people.

The standard frequency approach is widely used and has the benefit of being easily understandable by everybody. This is apparent in both the Merseyside and Midland Main Line examples, already discussed. However, get it wrong and it is always wrong. The easiest way out is to increase frequencies; once these reach perhaps every 15min but certainly every 10min, timetables become less constraining on the users.

To run services based on operational convenience is the least satisfactory, but is sometimes inevitable. If the traffic revenues, and potential traffic revenues, suggest that one train only can be justified, the challenge is to make the best use possible of that train. Sometimes interworking with other services may be possible, but that depends very much on location. Long isolated branches are likely to be the most susceptible to this problem. Thus the Middlesbrough-Whitby operation uses one train, which takes 85min to cover the 35 miles. The train calls at 15 intermediate stations, at one of which it has to reverse. It makes four return trips in the course

of the day, and is on the move for 11hr 20min out of a traffic day which lasts for 13hr 26min, or 84% of the time. Within that, there is some scope for meeting local preferences, but not much. One can arrive in Whitby at 08.47 for an 09.00 start, but the afternoon trains leave at either 16.05 or 19.13 — and that is it. Additionally, there is a modest commuter service over the five miles between Middlesbrough and Nunthorpe.

Techniques

There are a few useful dodges which can be used in timetable planning. One example is the 'bounceback'.

Peak-hour provision of commuter services is a costly business because of the low utilisation of the rolling stock and the staff who crew the train. Typically, the train leaves the carriage sidings for the suburban terminal as empty stock. Here it takes up its journey and runs in service to the city terminus. In this operation, it becomes increasingly well filled as the journey progresses. After that, well, nothing. The train has to be stabled for the day. In the evening, the same thing happens in reverse. If that is all that can be achieved, 250 days a year, the productivity is very poor.

However, if the train leaves the sidings early, starting its journey to town at say 07.00, it may arrive there at 07.40. After allowing passengers 5min to detrain, and rather than return calling at all stations in service, the train is 'bounced back' to the origin. It might achieve this, running empty, in 30min nonstop. It is then ready to start a second journey in at perhaps 08.20, to arrive at the city end at 09.00. 'Bounceback' has effectively doubled productivity all round, by allowing a second journey to be made within fairly closely defined time limits.

There will only be some services to which this technique can be applied, but it is well worth having wherever it can be arranged. It is approaches like this which are used to try and cope with occasional peaks, such as those associated with sporting or other events. Retaining trains at full 12-car or eight-car peak strength all day, rather than dropping down to four cars, can produce a lot of additional capacity at small cost. Idle rolling stock earns no revenue; giving it and the driving staff something constructive to do at least offers a chance of bringing in some fares receipts.

Timetable Planning

The responsibility for producing the railway timetable rests with Railtrack. The timetable seeks to accommodate the different and often conflicting wishes of all the various train operators. Services need to be timed so that all types of train, from the high-speed passenger train to the stopping passenger and the slower-moving freight, can be found a path.

The time that a train takes to run from one point to another will vary according to the rate of acceleration, maximum speed, braking characteristics, power/weight ratios, number of intermediate stops, and so on. These are matters for the operator, who is responsible for specifying the necessary service requirements. Then there are the conflicts with other trains, including at junctions, which further limit line capacity. Track maintenance may from time to time also be a constraint. These are for Railtrack to determine.

This information becomes the basis of each company's formal access bid to Railtrack. Many timetables are repetitive, in the sense that the same series of movements takes place at hourly intervals, and that train types and formations in the same service group vary little. Thus, if a basic service pattern can be agreed for one hour, much of the rest will slot into place.

Nevertheless, on a congested network with three or four different operators, all with their own ideas, the timetable planner may have to make several iterations in an attempt to resolve potential conflicts. Ultimately, it may be impossible. A less adversarial and a more co-operative approach is now becoming apparent.

A new passenger timetable is issued twice a year, in May and September, to deal with the changing seasonal demand.

In any new timetable, different services will have a different status. Some will be the subject of contracts, and to that extent the operating company can insist on their inclusion in more or less their existing form. Some, perhaps most, passenger services will form part of the Passenger Service Requirement of the Franchising Director. These too have a high priority. Others, such as open access services, are lower in the pecking order.

Services are reviewed in the light of experience, and consideration is given to various factors which affect the timing of each train. The results have to take the following into account.

Matters primarily for the TOCs:
• Planned origin, calling points and destination of each and every train.
• Proposed timings at and/or point-to-point running times between all stations throughout the journey.
• Length of station stops based on the number of passengers likely to be loading or unloading; longer stops are needed for peak trains.
• Connectional requirements into and out of other services.
• Traction and rolling stock to be used, to include developments such as new motive power of higher performance levels.
• Length of train.
• Maximum speed and brake force.
• Platform lengths; longer trains with automatic doors are not permitted to stop at stations with short platforms.

- The economical use of train crew, locomotives and rolling stock.
- The need for the coupling or uncoupling of trains, and where.
- Turn-round times needed for each type of train at terminating stations, to enable platform, servicing or other requirements to be met.
- Special requirements at stations such as staff availability, water for restaurant cars and lavatories or the need for the internal cleaning of passenger vehicles.

Matters primarily for Railtrack:
- The capacity of particular sections of railway, decided by:
    the varying performance of different types of train;
    the number of running lines available;
    the signalling methods in use;
    track gradients;
    requirements for movements within station limits;
    conflicting movements over junctions.
- Timing headways: the intervals between trains within the limits of the signalling system.
- The shortest headway needed to enter a platform after the previous train has left.
- Signalbox opening hours: some signalboxes close overnight.
- Allowances for track maintenance, engineering work, the effects of mining subsidence or poor condition of track, which may necessitate speed restrictions.
- Allowance for contingencies such as signalling failures or vandalism.
- Developments such as track improvements which may increase the maximum permitted speed at certain points of the journey.

Once all the information is collected, it is fed into the PROTIM computer system, which is a general train planning system. This produces the first draft timetables.

A careful check is then made. The paths laid down for each train must be practicable in relation to other trains through stations and junctions and there must be an acceptable interaction between passenger services and freight workings. This can be tested by plotting the draft schedule on graphs, based on a list of stations at the side and time against the bottom line. As the graph is drawn, any conflicting movements are noticed immediately and alterations can

be made. Where two trains appear unavoidably at the same spot at the same time, a 'pathing allowance' is added to the total running time allowed between the nearest timing points.

When details have been assimilated and checked, the whole is then fed into the national Train Service Data Base (TSDB). This database then produces the final public and working timetables in the various formats required.

Case study of service provision: The Far North line
A distance of 147 miles and more than 3hr travelling time north of Inverness, the three-trains-a-day Far North line reaches Georgemas Junction. This is a single-track mixed-traffic railway with passing loops at half the intermediate stations, of which there are 20. Maximum line speed is 75mph. Trains stop intermediately by request only, which helps to reduce overall journey times. At Georgemas, ScotRail trains for Wick (14 miles) may proceed straight ahead, but there is a trailing junction for Thurso (7 miles). Running times beyond Georgemas are 17min to Wick and 10min to Thurso. The train crew depot is at Wick.

Thurso is also the railhead for the ferry terminal for the Orkney Isles. How can an economical rail service best be provided to both these two small towns? Thurso is nowadays much the more important destination, due to tourists bound for Orkney and the growth of the town as its industries (Dounreay and Norfrost) overtook the traditional economic significance of fishing at Wick.

Traditionally, locomotive-hauled trains divided at Georgemas Junction; the problem was that a second locomotive and train crew were needed for the short journey thence, and there was precious little other work for them.

Right:
Gerrards Cross sees No 165007 depart for Marylebone on 12 November 1998. The down platform, on the right, was originally a down loop. The up platform is a new construction, which has pushed the up line some distance towards the down as it now exists. The effects of the changes in track geometry can be seen in the distance.
Author

Today's answer, using Class 156 Sprinter two-car units, is to run from Inverness to Georgemas Junction, reverse, proceed to Thurso and reverse again to continue to Wick. The return journey from Wick to Inverness similarly operates via Thurso. To aid the economics, the Georgemas Plunger allows the train driver to operate the points at that location. Otherwise, the line is Radio Electronic Token Block (RETB) controlled from Inverness.

Who wins and who loses from the present arrangements? Journey times between Inverness and Wick are extended by about 20min as a result of the diversion, but the towns do gain a direct service between each other.

Railway expenses are also reduced, since no more than one train is needed on each occasion.

However, life is rarely so simple, and this takes no account of the train capacity required. Usage of the 17.20 from Inverness has increased with the introduction of the 07.03 Dingwall to Inverness commuter service in spring 1998. The 17.20 is formed of two Class 156 units, and both proceed to Wick via Thurso.

The following morning, only one unit returns as the 06.00 from Wick. The second unit leaves Wick at 09.55 for Georgemas

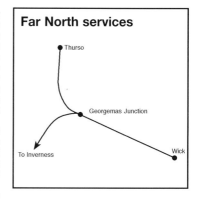

Far North services

Thurso

Georgemas Junction

To Inverness

Wick

only, where it meets the 07.00 service from Inverness at 10.23. It can be used from Wick to provide a connection to Thurso, but it also takes passengers arriving from Inverness directly to Wick, where it arrives at 10.43. The 07.00 from Inverness proceeds to Thurso and terminates there at 10.36.

There are now trains at both Wick and Thurso to form the midday service to the south. The unit from Wick leaves at 12.05, and the unit from Thurso at 12.10. They are coupled at Georgemas, from which they

leave for Inverness as a four-car formation at 12.30. This also provides a direct Wick to Inverness through train. Both the four-car services are needed in the summer months to serve destinations such as Culrain (for Carbisdale Castle Youth Hostel) or Forsinard (RSPB reserve), and also to increase local leisure use. This includes holders of the Highland Railcard, who now qualify for one third off the Highlands Days Out group fare.

The whole of this ScotRail operation is decidedly ingenious. It is designed to meet defined commercial requirements at minimal operational cost, given a rather awkward network problem. Further details can be found in Table 239 of the summer 1999 National Timetable.

There is as yet no commitment by ScotRail, but a Class 158 Express unit was trialled on the line in May 1999.

Freight priority — or not?

Concern at the priority given to improving the lot of the freight operator has been expressed by the Piggyback Consortium, who have bemoaned Railtrack's apparent lack of interest in making the necessary standard gauge enhancements in the WCML upgrading for piggyback traffic to be carried. A comparison of various gauges is shown in the diagram.

Essentially, the Piggyback Consortium seeks to see standard lorry trailers carried on rail wagons in the UK. 'Standard' is the key issue here, meaning 4m-high trailers. This is not possible within the normal British loading gauge, but could be achieved at some cost for which grant assistance from the government might be forthcoming. Despite earlier enthusiasm for gauge enhancement as part of the WCML upgrade, Railtrack's ardour now seems to have cooled. However, rail freight is experiencing strong growth at 10% or so a year, and in 20 years' time it is conceivable that an eight-fold increase in volumes might take place. This would triple the freight market share of rail, to which could be added that generated from growth.

This leads into three questions about railway infrastructure:

• what investment is needed to increase line capacity?
• how will it be financed?
• how will the line capacity made available be allocated?

On many routes, there are likely to be the passenger services run according to the Franchising Director's PSR, additional services run commercially by the same operator, competitive services from other operators, fast and relatively light freight, and the slower, heavy freight services. Some of these markets may be flexible in timings. Others will not be. Freight operations might be accommodated more easily on other routes, an option not readily available for the passenger businesses. Try telling commuters travelling to work in central Birmingham that it would suit the railway better if they arrived before 06.00, and also if they lived somewhere else!

Are some operators in a position to pay a premium to Railtrack to secure their own ends, and to what extent is forward commitment on access requirements important? What priority, if any, needs to be given to passenger services termed as 'socially necessary', or the PSR services which passenger operators are required to run as part of their franchise agreements? In the Piggyback Consortium's spokesman's words, 'Can Railtrack be trusted to act as the guardian of the network?'

The Strategic Rail Authority will have network capacity high on the agenda. It is the key to the expanding railway, while the linking of timetable paths to make overall sense is an art in itself.

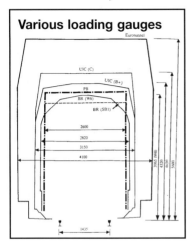

Various loading gauges

Eurotunnel

UIC (C)

UIC (B+)

PB

BR (W6)

BR (SB1)

2600

2820

3150

4100

1435

'It was quite an anticlimax when we got the engines, started the timetable and had to ground the lot for several weeks because the axles went round faster than the wheels.' G. F. Fiennes on the 'Britannia' Pacifics, delivered new to the Great Eastern section in 1951.

The reliability of the service provided depends upon:

- the robustness of the operating plan;
- the adequacy of the resources committed to its achievement;
- the availability and performance of the rolling stock; and
- the staff of the operating company and associated organisations such as Railtrack, and their motivation.

Resources

No operation can be successful without resources; these need to be sufficient to do the job intended, but as so often, a little leeway is desirable. For although the manager may have sufficient resources to do the job on paper, those resources need to be available at the right time and in the right place.

Consider the following. A rostered locomotive for a train from Trafford Park Freightliner terminal fails; the nearest available replacement and in a fit state is at Crewe. In itself, that is of no help. Can it be

8.

Executing the Operational Plan

used? If the failure in Manchester actually took place an hour or so previously, the locomotive in Crewe could have been worked over the 30 or so miles to cover, without any loss of time. For that, train crew who have signed for the route are required.

Solving this sort of problem needs to be done with the minimum of traffic disruption to the railway. But it also needs to take account of trainmen's duty schedules, as well as how to cover the job which the locomotive at Crewe was supposed to be doing next. It was to grapple with day-to-day incidents such as this that the Control organisations were invented.

Control Organisations

Traffic control has undergone many changes since it was introduced at Rotherham Masborough on the Midland Railway in

Right:
A Class 47 displays its front end connections: from the left, these are air brake pipe, vacuum pipe, the coupling, air reservoir pipe, steam heating pipe and air brake pipe. The date is 10 June 1985 and the place Temple Mills. Only the unkindest would point out that it has been derailed.
Peter Ashton

1907 by Cecil Paget, the then General Superintendent. This was to counter chronic freight unpunctuality and general line congestion in South Yorkshire and Derbyshire. The initial role of Control was to improve the use of both locomotives and train crews, thus leading to the better utilisation of wagons and shorter transit times. The role evolved to include passenger services and most other aspects of train operation; it now manages the day-to-day operation of the railway.

With the separation of the railway, Railtrack became responsible for the provision of the track, signalling and associated infrastructure to operate the timetable. The passenger and freight operating companies supply and manage the resources to operate the trains; they alone have a direct interface with the customers. This includes the provision of information on services.

As electrification spread throughout the country, a network of Control Offices was also established to oversee the OHLE and third-rail networks.

To this has been added personnel to co-ordinate the other aspects of the infrastructure.

The key objective is to ensure that the planned timetable service is operated punctually and efficiently. In the event of an unplanned incident, Railtrack is responsible for restoring the service in the most expeditious manner, liaising with the operating companies and any outside organisation which may have been involved. This might include, for instance, the emergency services. TOC Controls may have a Resources Controller and a Train Running and Passenger Information Controller; they do not have direct responsibility for the safety of the line, which is down to Railtrack.

Services are continually monitored to ensure compliance with the timetable, and any reasons for delays of 3min or more are allocated and signed off by the organisation responsible. A balance is compiled every four-weekly financial period; the penalty varies by time of day and the 'peak' costs more to reflect the presumed earning power of the train.

Most causes of delays are agreed currently, but a small number may have to await further investigation if the reason is not immediately apparent. For example, take a derailment. This might have been caused by a track defect, by a fault concerning the vehicle itself, or excessive speed by the train driver. More than one of these causes may have contributed.

It can assist communications if Railtrack and operating company personnel are co-located, but this is often not the situation. One constricting element is that in many places there are several TOCs and FOCs providing services. Nevertheless, the current Railtrack proposals to establish a number of strategically positioned Network Management Centres could help bring about a more integrated approach.

The Rule Book

The Rule Book is subdivided into sections to enable versions which are directly relevant to the responsibilities of different categories of staff, by grade and by function, to be produced:

A	General safety and security responsibilities.
B	Safety when walking and when working near running lines, and general.
C	Signals.
D	Passing signals at danger, wrong direction working.
H	Working of trains.
J	Shunting.
K	Trains or vehicles, detained on running lines or loops.
M	Accidents and failures.
N	Single line working.
R/T	Engineers' responsibilities and protection of work.
U	Temporary and emergency speed restrictions.

Right:
A Class 442 Wessex Electric set at Dorchester South on 28 February 1989 displays the lower skirt at the front end which acts as a cowcatcher for these units. Peter Ashton

The Rule Book Appendix, formerly the General Appendix, covers the detail of the following topics:

1	Accidents, incidents, bad weather.
2	Working of trains, general.
3	Working of trains, by type.
4	Power-operated doors.
5	Central locking of doors.
6	Automatic brake.
7	Auto couplers.
8	Automatic Warning System (AWS)
9	Level crossings.
10	Single lines.
11	MU Classes 101-128 and 302-312.
12	Engineers' on-track machines.
13	Departmental wagons.
14	Rail-mounted and self-propelled maintenance machines.
15	Securing of points, both new and redundant.

Finally, the Sectional Appendix is specific to each section of line, and covers the following:

- distances
- stations
- refuge sidings
- crossings
- train loading route availability restrictions
- signalboxes
- loops
- speed limits
- track circuit block or absolute block

There is also a working manual for rail staff, which contains items such as loading and conveyance of freight traffic, instructions for the conveyance of dangerous goods and working of freight trains. Separate instructions cover ac and dc electrified lines.

It is not practicable to discuss all these topics, so a few have been selected.

Driver-only Operation (DOO)

The operation of trains without a guard is specially authorised over certain sections of line. Different requirements apply to passenger trains DOO(P) and non-passenger services DOO(NP). The latter include freight, Royal Mail services, empty coaching stock and light engine movements.

In the case of passenger operation, services must be formed from trains with power-operated doors.

Other requirments are that:
● the train must be capable of stopping automatically should the driver become incapacitated
● the area of operation must have a means of continuous monitoring of trains such as track circuits, and
● a radio link *must* be provided to enable direct communication between the driver and signalman (or radio operator) in the signalling centre

Above:
This is the Shap Hardendale Quarry sidings, on the up side of the line. Provision for private sidings need not be extensive, though the train from which the photograph was taken was held for 10min or so as a result of a freight shunting across to the down line. The date is 18 March 1998.
Author

There must also be a radio link to enable the person at the signalling centre to communicate with customers on board the train in the event of the driver being unavailable.

An alternative to radio communication in case of failure might be the use of the mobile phones of revenue staff.

To enable drivers to view safely the full length of the train at station platforms without leaving the cab, provision is made for mirrors or cctv cameras and enhanced lighting. At some busier stations where platform staff are retained, it is usual to provide instructions to drivers by means of a CD (for close door) display adjacent to the signal head. This is activated from the platform, and it can subsequently be altered to RA (right away) when station duties are completed.

DOO(NP) operations do not require a direct radio link. The driver has the use of the National Radio Network (NRN) on many locomotives, or otherwise at the signalpost telephone on the lineside. At terminals, a member of staff in the form of a shunter, or a direct radio link, will be made available to provide assistance with shunting operations, train preparation and brake tests.

The Air and Vacuum Brakes

Locomotives, passenger and parcels vehicles and most freight rolling stock are fitted with an automatic brake. The air brake has been standardised throughout Britain, though a few older vehicles, both passenger and freight, still employ the vacuum brake system. These include some of the remaining Mk1 and early Mk2 stock, though others have been converted to air or are dual fitted with both air and vacuum brakes.

The automatic brake must be in use on every vehicle, but if a defect develops which results in a brakes being isolated in traffic, the train may be allowed to proceed to its destination or to a suitable location for attention. Depending on the position of the vehicle affected, the train may be subjected to certain restrictions, such as a much-reduced maximum speed.

A small number of vehicles are fitted with a through brake pipe only. This conveys the air supply, but does not act on the brakes on that vehicle. Such vehicles must therefore be marshalled in trains between fully braked vehicles.

Passenger, parcels and empty coaching stock services formed from air-braked vehicles normally operate with both the brake pipe and main reservoir pipe in use throughout the train. Freight services operate under the single pipe brake system. The normal working pressure of the brake pipe is 72.5psi (5 BAR) and the main reservoir pipe is normally maintained between 85 and 105psi (5.9 and 7.3 BAR). The brake-pipe coupling heads are coloured red, while the main reservoir coupling heads are yellow (except for a few vehicles in international traffic which are white). The brake is applied by exhausting air from the brake pipe.

The vacuum brake system requires a vacuum pressure of at least 20in but not more than 21in to be registered in the leading cab to release the train brakes. The brakes are applied by destroying the vacuum to allow the inrush of air.

A brake continuity test must be carried out to ensure that the brake pipe is coupled continuously throughout the train and that the required brake pipe pressure can be maintained. This is carried out on each occasion the locomotive is attached, vehicles are coupled or uncoupled (unless detached from the extreme rear of the train), or the train is reversed by the driver changing ends. Brake tests are also needed after a defect has been rectified or where a train has been left unattended and the traction unit shut down.

Coupling of Vehicles

A variety of couplings are employed to join vehicles. The most basic is the three-link coupling in which the bottom coupling link on one vehicle is lifted to rest on the drawbar hook of the adjacent vehicle and is retained there by gravity. Advanced systems include the Tightlock and BSI standard couplings which are fully automatic and include air brake pipe and electrical connections. Other types used in this country are screw, Instanter, drop-head buckeye and Alliance buckeye couplers. Some vehicles which are permanently coupled within a set such as many modern multiple-units and Freightliner wagons employ a bar coupling.

In addition to the basic coupling which provides the strength for the physical link, there may also be brake pipes, electrical train heating and lighting circuits and, on older vehicles, steam heating pipes between vehicles.

The manual coupling and uncoupling of trains is time consuming, difficult and can be a dangerous task; hence the moves towards greater automation. When coupling manually, after first ensuring that both vehicles are secured to prevent movement, the coupling is attached to the adjacent vehicle. Any heating connections are coupled, and finally the brake pipes are attached and the brake valves opened. This reduces the risk of the vehicle being able to move while a person is on the track between the vehicles. Uncoupling is carried out in the reverse order. Modern rolling stock employing Tightlock and BSI couplings are coupled and uncoupled by the driver from within his cab, without the need for any assistance. Buckeye couplers, while still automatic, need a manual intervention to attach brake pipes and heating connections.

Adaptor couplers are provided to enable Class 43 HST power cars without buffers on their outer ends, and multiple-unit trains fitted with Tightlock or BSI couplings, to be coupled to a conventional drawhook in an emergency. Tightlock couplers may also be coupled to certain buckeye couplers. Adaptor couplings are conveyed on HST power cars and some DMUs, but for other units an adaptor must be obtained from a maintenance depot.

Locomotives may be coupled in tandem or multiple. Coupled in tandem means a driver is required for each locomotive; in multiple means coupled for through control by one driver. Certain locomotives such as Class 59 and 60 may be coupled in multiple only with locomotives of the same class. Groups such as Class 56 and Class 58, or Classes 86/4, 86/5, 86/6 and 87 may be coupled in multiple within the same class and within the group. Likewise, DMUs of Classes 141-144, 150/1, 150/2, 153, 155, 156, 158 and 159 can also be coupled within the group, as can EMUs of Classes 313 to 322. This is a technical matter relating to what is possible, rather than what might be seen normally in general operations.

Some trains are routinely coupled or uncoupled/attached or detached in service, while other movements take place in sidings or in depots. The Southern Railway and its successors were great exponents of the division of trains in service. Modern examples are the peak-hour SWT services on the Bournemouth main line. Thus the 17.15 from Waterloo divides at Southampton, the first portion running nonstop to Bournemouth, Poole and then stations to Weymouth. The rear portion calls at intermediate stations to Poole and terminates there.

Where movements are scheduled to take place on running lines, provision is normally made in the signalling arrangements to include position light signals in colour-light signalling areas. In semaphore areas, the equivalent is the calling on or shunt ahead signal.

'There are three kinds of lies: lies, damned lies and statistics.' Benjamin Disraeli.

9.

Measurement of Achievement

This is an information society, and data is now relatively easily available to a business in all sorts of forms. This is as true of the railway as other organisations; part of the skill is knowing what measures are the most useful for, in the present case, operational purposes. A Train Operating Company is used to illustrate the various statistics which might be used.

If you do not know what you are achieving, you cannot meet targets or measure performance.

This chapter is structured to consider first the basic measurements which can be made and what they demonstrate, and secondly the performance related derivatives.

Throughout, readers should bear in mind the period over which measurements are made, and the variations inherent within them. In particular, railway accounting is based on a four-weekly period, rather than calendar months. The result is that each period results are for a constant 28 days, though the incidence of bank holidays and the like is not regular.

Secondly, seasonal variations will mask underlying trends. A fall in the sales of tickets to seaside destinations is only to be expected as the autumn draws on; it does not in itself indicate any product weakness. The more telling results tend to be the moving annual

averages, which smooth out the results of the previous 13 four-weekly periods, so that underlying trends are more readily apparent.

Thirdly, revenues from ticket sales are recorded as they are received, but they may impose a substantial future obligation on the operator. There is a well-documented rise in annual season ticket sales in the period immediately after Christmas and the New Year, as commuters try and beat what are now the traditional January fares increases. So much is good news for the operator, represented by money in the bank, but revenues for the rest of the year will be that much lower.

Ticketing has been used here only as an example of the variations which can arise; the same kind of analysis can be applied to many other fields.

Right:
Passengers join the 10.09 Birmingham International to Glasgow Central train at Preston on 17 September 1993. Even with the extra width of these doors compared with the standard earlier versions, loading can still be painfully slow for passengers with any amount of luggage. *Author*

Basic Measurements

Resources

- Trains. The number of vehicles on lease, subdivided into diesel locomotives, electric locomotives, HST power cars, diesel multiple-units, electric multiple-units, coaching stock and service vehicles. Further subdivisions are immediately apparent such as the TOPS class of each locomotive. When it comes to passenger-carrying vehicles, it must be remembered that multiple-units are just that, and each consist of between one and five vehicles. This is important when computing seating capacity.
- Stations. Separately, the number leased from Railtrack, the number for which access charges are paid to another TOC, and access charges paid to Railtrack for its own managed stations.
- Staff. Their numbers expressed as full-time equivalents, by grades and function.

Operations

- Loaded train miles. Shows the total production in terms of travel opportunities made available for sale.
- Train miles. Those produced including empty stock workings, which reflect the work undertaken by train crews.
- Route miles run over. Indicates the total spread of service provision, though it makes no reference to the frequency of such service.
- Proportions of trains arriving on time, and proportions cancelled. These punctuality and reliability statistics are presently key indicators of franchise performance.

Sales

- Passenger journeys. This can be derived from ticket sales, after making allowance for the calculations necessary to establish a figure for season tickets and for travelcards and similar. Care also needs to be taken on the attribution of return tickets issued at the originating station and those issued elsewhere. Ticket sales will also show type of ticket and class of travel. A further division needs to be made between the TOCs concerned if journeys can be made by more than one company and the ticket is interavailable.
- Passenger revenue. As passenger journeys; similar problems arise.
- Passenger miles (or km). This is the most

frequently used single figure to express the volume of travel. It recognises that the volumes reflect not only the number of journeys which people make, but the length of each. One journey from King's Cross to Darlington by GNER equals 232 passenger miles, virtually the same as three journeys from King's Cross to Peterborough (3 x 76 miles = 228 miles). But whereas GNER is the only operator to Darlington, Peterborough services are provided also by WAGN. This can be derived from the point-to-point distances, multiplied by the number of journeys attributed to each flow.

Derivatives

Ten useful derivatives are suggested; others are always possible. Most are on a company-wide basis over the course of an accounting period. It is when information is wanted on a train-by-train, or day-by-day basis, that the problems really start mounting.

Specific information here can usually be obtained only by physical counting, eg of passengers joining each train at each station. This might be necessary, for instance, to assess an overcrowding problem. But there are further implications in terms of the costs of mounting such surveys, and for their subsequent analysis and interpretation.

Another method is by interview surveys, to find out where people came from, how they got to the station, their journey purpose, ultimate destination, their perception of service quality, and so on. A variation is the self-administered questionnaire, which can be given out to passengers or distributed by some other means. Such matters are firmly in the market research field, but such techniques can be of great use to a TOC in establishing hard information on the market which it is serving.

1. Receipts per loaded train mile.

This measure shows the average earning power of a train, which can be recorded on a regular basis to assess general trends. This needs to take into account the company policy on fare levels and the change in the value of money over time, as well as the mileage operated. This will change when new timetables are introduced.

2. **Receipts per passenger mile.** This is the nearest single measure to establishing how the amount spent for an average journey is changing over time. Falls in this figure could reflect a discounting policy by the TOC, or a move away from full fare travel.

3. **Passenger miles per loaded train mile.** This is the average trainload, or how many people are on the average train at any one time. Such figures may be dispiritingly low; if so, they may reflect a high peak usage and low off-peak carryings, but the cause is a matter for the company to examine further.

4. **Train miles per train crew staff member.** This is all train miles, whether loaded or empty. This is a measure of train crew productivity; is the result rising or falling?

5. **Average fare per passenger journey.** What does the average passenger pay for travel? The results will be an average of peak and off-peak, adult and child, etc. This is also an indication of whether journey lengths are changing over time.

6. **Train miles per locomotive/EMU set/DMU set/HST set.** This is an indication of reliability, but low figures might also suggest that fleet size is over-generous. Could the TOC make do with less?

7. **Operating expenses per train mile.** This is a major expenditure for the TOC which is fully under the company's control. Comparison with the corresponding receipts figures over time will show which way the business is heading.

8. **Maintenance expenses per train mile.** Similarly to the operating expenses, this is also an indication of the amount of work the rolling stock is requiring. A consideration of the age of the stock may be relevant.

9. **Loaded train miles per passenger vehicle.** How well used is the rolling stock and does it earn its keep? This measure indicates the fleet's daily usage when earning revenue.

10. **Terminal expenses per train call.** Terminals include all stations. Most TOCs have a fairly similar operation throughout, but are the variatitions which this measure reveals justified?

Purposes

In summary, statistics can help the manager to determine the volume of the output, and the receipts associated with it. They may also assist in calculating the cost or effort of providing that output.

Efficiency and quality measurements are both highly desirable, and in virtually every case the trends in the results over time are of substantial interest. Trends are a measurement of change.

Statistics do, however, have to be interpreted with care; do they really show what they at first seem to indicate? Cross-checking of results which intuitively seem wrong is always worth while. Thus, if the loaded train miles per passenger vehicle suddenly decline sharply, is that because

Right:
South West Trains' passengers await their morning peak service at Worcester Park on 19 April 1991. If only such loads could be persuaded to present themselves throughout the traffic day. *Author*

AdTranz have just delivered some of the TOC's new Turbostar sets, which have yet to enter traffic? Train miles unchanged, total vehicles much increased, yes, but this was entirely anticipated and is no reflection on performance. An obvious example has been chosen to illustrate the point, but other reasons for variations may be less apparent. Disraeli may have been at least half right!

Below:
Connex SouthCentral's No 455807 leaves the Caterham terminus for London Bridge on 9 February 1999. The RA indication on the signal T570 denotes that the station staff have given the driver the right away. A previous display would have been CD as an indication to the driver that the doors could be closed. *Author*

'It was no uncommon thing to take an engine out on the line to look for a late train that was expected, and many times have I seen the train coming and reversed the engine and run back out of the way as quickly as I could.' Diary of Sir Daniel Gooch, Locomotive Superintendent of the Great Western Railway 1837-64, referring to the early days.

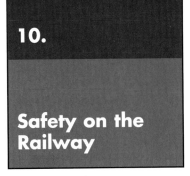

10.

Safety on the Railway

Safety Development

Railway safety has evolved over many years; Gooch himself commented that it was a marvel that the company escaped serious accidents with such practices. Others, however, were less fortunate, while the general expansion of the railway system began to raise some disquiet. An element of public control over the railway began with the Act of 1840, and the principal developments in this field over the years are given below. Together they give a feel for the way in which the legal aspects of operational matters developed over the years.

It should perhaps be mentioned that many of these Acts have since been repealed in whole or in part, but in the main their provisions have been re-enacted and sometimes strengthened in subsequent legislation.

Railway Regulation Act, 1840
This Act required the Board of Trade to be given notice of the intended opening of any

---

Above left:
Working on the railway takes many staff into places which are not over-safe, as in this case of a shunter adjusting the wagon brakes. While the record of the railway in train accidents has been good, that for staff undertaking tasks such as these was in the past quite poor. *BR/Author's collection*

Left:
Bridge bashing is quite a menace, not only because of the damage done but also the disruption to train services while Railtrack manages to get someone to the site to check whether trains can be allowed to pass. This is a well-protected railway underbridge at Ely, pictured on 8 November 1997; big wagons queue on the right to use the level crossing. *Author*

---

railway and gave them powers to postpone the opening if, after inspection, they were not satisfied that it could be operated without danger to the public. Trespass upon the railway became a criminal offence.

Railway Regulation Act, 1842
Serious accidents became reportable by the railway companies, whether they were attended by personal injury or not. All railway companies were put under an obligation to erect, maintain and repair fences along their lines. Drivers, guards, porters, signalmen and others conducting traffic on the railway, or maintaining it, were prohibited from being drunk while so employed.

Railway Clauses Consolidation Act, 1845
This Act made it a requirement to build a bridge where a railway crossed the highway, unless the authorising Act of the railway permitted the construction of a level crossing. Gatekeepers were to be employed to staff such crossings and operate the gates, but gates were normally to be kept closed across the road unless otherwise specially authorised. The railway had to provide and maintain level crossings used as footpaths and bridleways. It was also necessary for accommodation crossings to be provided where a landowner's property was divided by the construction of the railway, or occupation crossings where the private way was in common ownership. Railway companies became entitled to make by-laws.

Regulation of Railways Act, 1868
The installation of a means of communication between the passengers and the staff in charge of the train became

compulsory in all passenger trains travelling more than 20 miles without a stop.

Regulation of Railways Act, 1871
This Act specified the types of accident which were deemed to be reportable*, legalised the holding of formal accident inquiries by the Inspecting Officers and provided for the publication of their reports.

*Reportable accidents included all those to passenger trains, those to goods trains affecting passenger running lines, all cases of trains becoming divided or coupling failures on passenger running lines, mechanical failures which have caused or might cause an accident to a passenger train, all rail breakages on passenger running lines, and accidents to people.

Regulation of Railways Act, 1889
In this significant piece of legislation, the Board of Trade was authorised to make orders to impose:

• the block system of signalling on all passenger lines;
• the fitting of the continuous automatic brake on all passenger trains; and
• the interlocking of points with signals generally.

Under this Act, the passenger was required to produce a ticket or pay the fare on demand, and fare evasion became an offence.

Road and Rail Traffic Act, 1933
Railway undertakings were required to secure the authority of the Secretary of State for the opening of any new portion of a railway to passenger traffic, the opening of additional running lines to passenger traffic, or the opening of any railway for electric traction.

Transport Act, 1947
This, the Nationalisation Act, disallowed generally the operation of privately-owned wagons on the national network. Exempted were tank wagons and a somewhat bizarre list which included those specially constructed or set aside to carry goods such as bulk grain, cement, guns, night soil and sewage, propellers or salt. Privately-owned wagons were also permitted to be used on international services.

British Transport Commission Act, 1954
For the first time, lifting barriers were permitted to replace swing gates at level crossings, with the consent of the Minister.

British Transport Commission Act, 1957
The railway was no longer required to man highway crossings, thus permitting automatic half-barrier and no-barrier crossings, with suitable safeguards which included signing.

Transport Act, 1962
The railway ceased to be a common carrier,

under the terms of which no consignment could be refused and for the carriage of which the carrier's liability was effectively unlimited.

Transport Act, 1968
Grants for unremunerative passenger services were introduced, where there were social or economic reasons to justify them. The railway was required to introduce additional protection at road level crossings when so directed by the Minister.

Level Crossings Act, 1983
This allows the Secretary of State to make orders specifying in detail the protective equipment to be provided, and to give authority to alter or replace existing equipment.

Transport & Works Act, 1992
Powers for the authorisation and construction of railways, previously obtained through private Acts of Parliament, are now acquired

by an Order made under this Act. A local inquiry may be necessary before the Secretary of State gives his decision. This procedure does not apply to schemes deemed to be of national importance, and not at all in Scotland. This Act also introduced comprehensive provisions to control the use of alcohol and drugs for those working on the railway.

Railways Act, 1993
This Act establishes a licensing regime for the ownership and use of railway assets to provide passenger and goods services, and specifies how such licences might be modified. A railway facility owner is required to enter into access agreements with train operators which allow the operator to use the owner's facilities. The government is given the right to give directions to all those involved in service provision in time of hostilities or national emergency. Railway operators and others are given the status of statutory authorities. The Post Office can no

longer compel railways to carry mailbags. Penalty fares schemes are permitted, subject to regulation by the Secretary of State. The Railways Act, 1993 includes:

• Amendment to the Health & Safety at Work etc Act, 1974
Brings the proper construction and safe operation of the railways, their locomotives and rolling stock, and the protection of railway employees and the general public from personal injury and other risks, under the terms of this Act.

• Amendment to the Restrictive Trade Practices Act, 1976
Allows co-operation between railway operators over matters such as track access and ticketing to be exempted, to ensure that network benefits are achieved.

Railway Inspectorate

The above can be no more than a brief examination of how the legislative background has developed. Of perhaps more immediate consequence are the publications of Her Majesty's Railway Inspectorate (HMRI), now part of the Health & Safety Executive under the generic heading of 'Railway Safety Principles and Guidance'.

The objective of the Principles is to set out what the Railway Inspectorate would expect to see considered in railway works, plant and equipment to provide an acceptable level of safety for all those affected, whether passengers, employees or contractors. The safety principles are designed to ensure that all intolerable risks have been eliminated and that all remaining risks have been reduced to be as low as reasonably practicable (ALARP). But the effectiveness of this approach depends on determining what those risks are, measuring the level of exposure, and recording the safety performance, as well as taking the appropriate action.

Matters to be considered include:

- Operating conditions, from normal to emergency situations.
- Environmental conditions, such as fog, wind, rain, snow and flood.
- Fire, including risks, consequences and protective measures.
- Inspection and maintenance of works, throughout their lifetime.

The Principles are divided into six headings:

- infrastructure
- stations and stabling areas
- electric traction systems
- railway control systems
- level crossings
- trains.

The problem of the level crossing is now examined in some detail.

Level Crossings

The level crossing is a function of the geography of Britain, in the sense that it is a much more common feature in the flatter lands of the eastern counties of England than it is, say, in the Pennines.

Level crossings, together with those for use by pedestrians and/or farm vehicles only, are essentially an undesirable feature.

They provide a point of conflict between trains and (primarily) road users; some degree of protection has to be afforded to both. While a reduction in the number of crossings has been carried out with some success on major routes such as the East Coast main line, the reality is that most will remain on the system for the foreseeable future. Closure for most is not an option. This is against a background of higher speeds on the railway, on a network which will hopefully be considerably busier in the future than it is today, and an ever more congested road network.

There are nearly 10,000 crossings of all types, including footpaths, in use on the Railtrack network. The situation (in 1993) may be summarised as shown overleaf:

As in other fields of railway activity, accidents have been a source of lessons. Among these was that at Hixon automatic half-barrier crossing in 1968, when an abnormal load (a transformer) travelling at 2mph was hit by the 11.30 Manchester Piccadilly to London Euston. Neither the Police accompanying the load nor the vehicle driver telephoned the signalman before crossing. It was found that the road vehicle could not possibly have cleared the crossing within the 24sec warning of an approaching train given at that time. Eleven people died and 44 were injured.

Level Crossing Types

Protected crossings		
Manually controlled, with gates or barriers	1,137	11.7%
Automatic crossings, half-barriers or monitored	657	6.7%
Total protected crossings	1,794	18.4%
Unprotected crossings		
User worked, with gates or barriers, but unmanned	5,657	58.2%
Open and footpath crossings	2,277	23.4%
Total unprotected crossings	7,934	81.6%
All crossings	9,728	100.0%

Modern crossings are designed to reduce delays to the road user and, often, to allow economies of operation to the railway. They are also reliable. However, they are also frequently opposed in local consultation before, for instance, an automatic half-barrier crossing is introduced. A heavy wooden gate may look safe, designed as it is to stop a galloping horse. But, as the author well remembers being told, if a train hits that, you have a large and heavy missile flying through the air as well as the danger caused by the train itself.

The real problem is that a modern crossing significantly transfers the responsibility for safety from the railway to the road user. Today, the majority of accidents are caused by errors or deliberate actions on the part of the motorist. Part of the level crossing designer's skill must be in minimising the consequences of road user error. During research for HMRI, motorists who had been identified as ignoring the red signals at level crossings were interviewed. A total of 55% admitted that they had deliberately driven over the crossing when they should have stopped and a further 27% had failed to recognise it as a level crossing.

Present actions include cutting back of vegetation to improve sighting, whistle boards to give audible notice of the approach of a train, keeping road markings and road surfaces maintained to a high standard, educating the local community to safe use, and upgrading the equipment provided, such as telephones at private level crossings used by vehicles. Crossing closure is the preferred option and has been pursued where 90mph running has been introduced. As can be seen from the table, user-worked crossings represent the huge majority, though the level of use is likely to be relatively low in many cases.

Other action has been to interlock railway signalling with level crossing gates so that a rail signal must show a stop aspect to train drivers when the gates or barriers are open to the road, or to automate the level crossing.

Technically, level crossings are primarily a problem for Railtrack, but in reality they are a difficulty for the railway industry as a whole.

HMRI Principle 23 states that level crossings should be safe for users and trains. Where a right of way crosses the railway at track level, appropriate arrangements should be provided to warn and protect level crossing users, and safeguard the railway. A number of factors for consideration are then listed:

- The types of level crossing users and the frequency and speed of expected rail, road and pedestrian traffic.
- The uniform visual appearance of each type of level crossing.
- The possibility of slow or abnormal road traffic using the level crossing.
- The type of road or path on either side of the level crossing.
- The need to deter trespass and straying on to the railway.
- The protection of the level crossing by the signalling system.
- The effect of equipment failure on the safety of trains and level crossing users.
- The arrangements to avoid danger if a level crossing user is trapped.
- The need for local operation.
- The interface with any electric traction system.

The specialised Guidance on level crossings is set out in Part 2 Section E of the Railway Safety Principles, which itself extends to 72 pages. It should be stressed that these are principles which are intended to give advice; they do not set an absolute standard.

Readers will conclude from the foregoing, rightly, that level crossings collectively have caused more problems in recent times than many other parts of the railway. They are also a high-profile matter when it comes to public interest since many of the public, often as car drivers, find that they are directly affected.

Railway Safety Case Regime

The following enhancements to the statutory safety regime were considered necessary by the HSE as a result of railway privatisation:

- Train operators, station operators and Railtrack should be equipped and organised so that risks to safety are controlled effectively.
- Staff competencies should be ensured.
- Safety must be ensured at the interfaces between train operators, station operators and Railtrack.
- There must be a control over the movement of dangerous goods by rail.

The Railway (Safety Case) Regulations 1994 require each group to prepare a safety case and to have it accepted by another body. Railtrack validates the operators' safety cases; the HSE validates that of Railtrack. The safety cases must then be implemented. The Regulations concentrate on the need to establish whether each of the bodies has the will, capabilities, resources, organisation and systems to operate safely right from the start.

Safety cases must contain:

- basic operational information, such as a description and specification of the system;
- the safety policy statement; and
- a risk assessment: what are the principal hazards?

It must also include descriptions of the arrangements for safety management, monitoring and audit, training and competence of staff, project management, and control of contractors.

The Railways (Safety Critical Work) Regulations 1994 require that staff such as train drivers are competent and fit, and that records of their assessment are kept and available for inspection. There is a general duty on employers to prevent fatigue which might lead to an increase in risk levels.

The Carriage of Dangerous Goods by Rail Regulations 1994 set out a new statutory framework to control the carriage of dangerous goods, establishing a chain of responsibility. They cover the design, strength, construction, suitability and the labelling and marking of wagons and containers. Also covered are their certification and maintenance, plus provisions for safe loading, segregation, fire, explosion and crew training.

Performance

There are three types of railway accident, which are defined as follows:

- Train Accident. What is often thought of popularly as a railway accident, this includes collisions and derailments, fires and running into obstructions.
- Movement Accident. These are the accidents in which a train is involved, such as boarding and alighting incidents or passengers falling out of train doors, staff being caught between vehicles while coupling or uncoupling them, persons struck by a train at a level crossing or staff working on the track.
- Non-Movement Accident. These accidents have no real railway connotation other than they took place on railway premises. Included in this group are slips, trips and falls, especially on stairs or escalators, being struck by a platform barrow, or staff injured when using tools.

Such accidents will vary in severity, and their incidence will vary between passengers (and those meeting them), railway staff (including contractors), and third parties such as the staff of station food outlets or bookstalls. All have business to be where they are on railway premises; another category of accident is that to trespassers and suicides.

Broadly, deaths are most numerous in movement accidents, but both major and minor injuries are found most often in the non-movement accidents. The chance of a passenger being killed or seriously injured in a train accident is very low, but the rate rises with movement accidents and again with non-movement accidents.

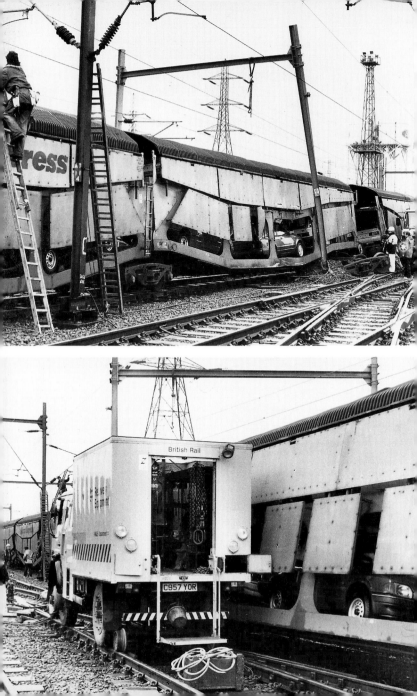

Of the causes of train accidents, about half the total are caused by running into obstructions; here malicious acts by the public are the most numerous, followed by animals on the line. Accounting for a further quarter of incidents is fires on trains, again with nearly half of them caused maliciously but with almost as many caused by technical defects.

The remaining headings of collisions and derailments see staff taking the blame for about one third in each case, but whereas other derailments are put down mainly to the condition of the track, most other incidents classified as collisions take place because of the irregular opening of train doors by the public.

It is sad to record that in 1997/8 about 60% of train accidents were caused by malicious actions. This is not just a railway issue; there is a need for partnerships and concerted effort by all concerned. Every passenger and freight operating company needs a strategy, and there is a sound business case to tackle the problem.

The railway industry is expected to grow in the future. What problems might this bring? It is certainly arguable that more traffic without more capacity will bring more risk. There will be more signals approached, and perhaps passed, at danger. Station congestion will build up faster, which will make stations more difficult to evacuate if

needed. Level crossings will be closed to road traffic longer, which will add to road congestion and perhaps tempt more road vehicle drivers to weave around half-barriers. The whole of the railway system might become that much less forgiving of failures.

But if the higher capacity requirements are met with investment by Railtrack, who can then use the advantages of transmission-based signalling to offer greater line capacity in conjunction with an Automatic Train Protection (ATP) system, risk control should not be a problem. Does more traffic on rail imply less on road? The accident rates suggest that this would be a good move:

Safety of different transport modes

Average numbers killed or seriously injured, 1986-95 average, per billion passenger miles.

Air	.0.2
Rail	.3.3
Bus and Coach	.16.0
Water	.47.0
Car	.50.0
Motorcycle	.1,786.0

Source: HMRI

A rigorous safety management system is crucial to safety performance. However, the bureaucracy of risk analysis must not be allowed to run the system by stifling change, lengthening timescales, adding costs and encouraging future aversion to even low risk levels. The transport industry must be allowed to change and to develop over time. Risk analysis is essentially judgemental and requires the exercise of discretion. It cannot be based solely on statistical records. Account must also be taken of the costs of higher levels of safety achievement.

Her Majesty's Railway Inspectorate's interests are:

- approvals of new works
- acceptance of safety cases
- investigation
- inspection
- information and advice
- enforcement.

The principal aim is 'to secure the proper control of risks to the health and safety of employees, passengers and others who might be affected by the operation of Britain's railways'. To achieve this, HMRI seeks:

- to enforce the law;
- to take account of stakeholder aspirations, and to be accountable;
- to act in a proportionate manner;
- to be consistent in the approach to issues; and

- to target the areas of greatest risk or where they can make the most difference.

Finally, on personal safety, Merseytravel has undertaken much work on this subject. The PTE concluded that the presence of staff is central to passengers' feelings of safety, but that the staff themselves need to feel safe and able to deal with any threats. Young people have been found to be a major area of concern, as both victims and perpetrators of anti-social behaviour.

Merseytravel offers the chilling statistic that concern for personal safety leads passengers to use alternative forms of transport for 30% of journeys where public transport is an option. As with the malicious damage to the railway discussed above, this is a society problem and has to be dealt with on that basis, but it poses a very real revenue threat to each and every TOC.

Left:
The simplest of railway crossings are those such as bridleways; this is where the photographer is standing, quite legitimately, just beyond the end of the platforms of Chipstead station. The date is 9 February 1999. But why do we need such a crossing when there is a perfectly adequate station footbridge which could be used instead? The answer is precisely because it *is* a bridleway; horses don't take kindly to the footbridge steps. *Author*

Right:
The hand-worked swing gates of the traditional level crossing are diminishing in numbers. This example is the little used Park Lane Crossing, south of Theobalds Grove. It was photographed on 15 August 1997. This line is on the Southbury loop and is electrified at 25kV ac. *Author*

Below right:
The automatic half-barrier (AHB) crossing here is at Warehorne Lane, west of Ham Street station on the Ashford-Hastings line. The barriers are falling and the approaching train can already be heard in this quiet location. The road user has to rely on audio/visual warnings, as the foliage is such that the train cannot be seen before it arrives. This was photographed on 29 May 1999. *Author*

Left:
At Whyteleafe on the Caterham branch on 16 September 1998, the departing train is still in sight and the full barriers are yet to reach their fully vertical position. But the first vehicles are already half way across and the pedestrians have made a start.
Author

Centre left:
Perceptions of personal safety are not enhanced by this type of defacement. A modern and apparently recently installed shelter has been comprehensively attacked and at the other end of the platform the timetables have been rendered totally illegible. This is Caledonian Road & Barnsbury on 8 December 1998.
Author

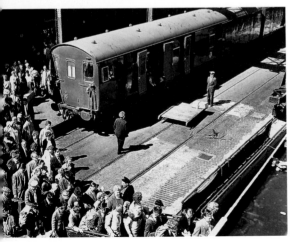

Below left:
Catching the boat from the train at Dover was like this on 18 August 1959, but one wonders if passengers would be allowed to mix with the train to this extent nowadays? Nobody seems to be likely to come to any harm. The rail vehicles are two of the Motor Luggage Vans which were designed to be detached from the train and move to the quaysides, just as shown here. They were equipped with traction batteries to allow them to work away from the third rail. *BR/Author's collection*

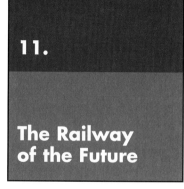

11

'Of Prism's four franchises, two are good and two are appalling. It seems to be doing all in its power to right the wrongs, but in railways, performance and profit do not necessarily run in tandem with one another.'
Tempus column, The Times, 8 June 1999.

Railways are a service industry, whose business efforts are always subject to the ebb and flow of the national economy and international trade. If one result is that employment levels fall in Glasgow, which has the largest commuter rail service network outside London, there is not a lot that the railway companies can do about it. Conversely, if they rise, passenger numbers increase almost magically, to the extent that they can become a downright embarrassment in service provision terms. Similar situations arise with freight; the railway may move the goods quickly and efficiently, but it cannot by itself have much say in whether or not the end user wants to buy them.

In no particular order, railway fortunes depend on:

- growth in the markets which they serve;
- increasing market share;
- raising the quality of service;
- creating a more saleable product;
- raising the volumes carried;
- providing more capacity;
- keeping unit costs down; and
- selling services profitably.

The Railway of the Future

Products and Costs

The largest railway infrastructure projects presently under way are the West Coast main line upgrade, the Channel Tunnel Rail Link and Thameslink 2000.

The West Coast main line is the most important trunk railway in Britain, but it is also one of the oldest. The most recent major works on it were the preliminaries to electrification, which was completed in a large number of stages between 1960 and 1967. The work north of Crewe formed a separate project, and this was completed in 1974.

The present upgrade being undertaken by Railtrack in conjunction with Virgin Trains promises to increase line capacity and line speeds. The operator is purchasing a fleet of high-performance tilting trains, the purpose of which is to allow higher curving speeds without discomfort to the passengers.

Right:
Extending platform lengths can meet with various degrees of difficulty, but Tunbridge Wells Central is in the 'very hard' category. To make the station suitable for accepting 12-car trains would need the platform extended into the tunnel at this, the southern end, or into the tunnel at the northern end. The view was taken on 21 September 1998.
Author

What does this mean for the main passenger operator?

Case study: Virgin West Coast plans

Besides a much-enhanced market potential, faster trains offer huge opportunities for productivity gains. At present, trains require roundly 2hr 30min (at best) from Manchester to Euston, plus an hour for turnround, and another 2hr 30min back again to Manchester followed by another 1hr turnround. The total round trip time is thus 7hr. This means that seven train sets are needed to provide an hourly service.

However, if a thoroughly reliable 2hr transit time from London to Manchester can be achieved, the turnround can be reduced to 30min. A round trip can then be made in 5hr, which reduces the number of train sets to five. This is equivalent to a 29% improvement in productivity.

This, though, is traditional thinking, which reduces resources to provide a given and predetermined capacity requirement. An altogether more attractive alternative is to *add* three train sets, making 10 trains in all. This enables Virgin to offer a half-hourly service between Manchester and London, or twice the present frequency, with only a 43% increase in resources. A similar approach offers a train every 15min between Birmingham and Euston.

Similar gains can be made in staff productivity. Today's driver may make a Manchester-Euston-Manchester return journey in a shift, which will take him around 6hr. If the return journey can be achieved in 4hr 30min, flexible rostering gives the opportunity to make *two* Manchester-London return journeys in an extended shift, and still provide an hour's rest break in the middle.

Taxpayers might question how much all this would cost, but one beauty of the new railway is that minimum requirements for future service provision are locked into a contractual arrangement. 'Extras' are a matter for Virgin Rail, whose contract promises a positive return to the government over the 15 years of the West Coast franchise.

Other productivity gains can be had from replacing all slam doors on coaching stock with power doors, which reduces platform labour requirements; on the other hand, more intensive on-board services require an increase in staff employment.

Higher speeds bring better utilisation for both staff and equipment, with more seat-km to sell — though the seats must be occupied.

New Stations

Many new stations have been opened since the mid-1970s. There may be more in the future, though it could also be argued that most of the best schemes have already been built.

A new station brings with it the opportunity for the railway to tap new custom and hence revenues. Thus, a station at East Garforth, 8 miles east of Leeds, was opened in 1987 to serve an expanding housing area. Despite being less than a mile from the long-established Garforth station, it quickly built up passengers, with over 800 journeys per day being recorded one year after opening. This is prime commuter

Above right:
Welwyn North station sees a DVT at the London end of an approaching up GNER express on 15 October 1998. As can be seen, the rear of the train has only just cleared Welwyn South Tunnel.
Author

Centre right:
The second bay platform at Willesden Junction Low Level has been taken out of use and to the best of the author's knowledge, no operator wishes to use it. The date is 27 October 1998. But restoration would be that much more difficult and also more costly as a result of the signal being placed in its present position.
Author

Below right:
Benfleet scores well as an LTS Rail station where disabled access has been treated seriously. The assistance of station staff is necessary to unlock the gate at the far end of the path. This picture was taken on 29 April 1999.
Author

DISABLED ACCESS
ONLY
TO BE ACCOMPANIED
BY
STATION STAFF

territory and represents the highest trip rates per thousand population for new stations in West Yorkshire.

New local stations will usually rely on an existing local operation to provide the train service; setting up a new operation altogether raises costs into a different league. Capital costs may have been met by outside parties, but stations still have to be maintained and administered. Such costs will be higher if it is to be staffed, but items such as lighting have to be provided in any event. How such costs are met will depend on the access agreement with Railtrack and the involvement or otherwise of local authority or, where appropriate, Passenger Transport Executive interests.

Case study: a new station at Digby & Sowton, Devon

Digby & Sowton, between Polsloe Bridge and Topsham, is on the Exeter-Exmouth branch about four miles out of Exeter. It was opened on 28 May 1995, with total project costs of £698,000. The station consists of a four-car single platform, an entrance building, a shelter and access ramp. Also included are foot and cycle paths, and a joint pedestrian and cycle overbridge.

The adjoining car park has 500 spaces. Capital costs were funded by Devon County

Council through a bid to government, and a grant of £200,000 from Tesco stores.

The idea of a station to serve the industrial areas at Sowton first appeared in the early 1980s, being promoted by Devon County Council in conjunction with a park-and-ride site for the industrial estate. Land was reserved for a small station with associated car parking and access road.

In the late 1980s, a regional shopping centre was proposed for an adjacent parcel of land (the old Digby mental hospital), and the station was included within these proposals. The regional shopping centre was not built due to economic recession, but Tesco bought the area and completed a superstore in 1994. Subsequently, a considerable amount of housing was zoned as well as further retail.

During the feasibility stage it was agreed that the best place it was not the original site reserved but one nearer the shopping development and houses, while still close to the industrial estate. Both Devon County Council and the TOC assessed the station as worth while in view of the developments. There were delays in starting because of the need for construction access over private land and the target for opening slipped.

Of the total cost, only about 50% was actual civils work. The rest was design fees,

construction management costs, possession costs and contingencies. Railtrack required a formal legal agreement which emerged as a three-year tripartite agreement between Devon County Council, the TOC and Railtrack. This covered land issues, level of services and pricing arrangements, construction management including specification change procedure, stage payments, car parking and funding. Initially, the TOC were reluctant to stop all existing trains but agreed eventually with some caveats on peak capacity.

Full Devon County Council approval was obtained in October 1994. This included a DCC-designed and managed entrance building and forecourt on DCC land. Digby & Sowton opened on time, with the start of the 1995 summer timetable. Usage built up steadily from the start, with both the TOC and Devon County Council being pleased with the results. A total of 20,000 passenger journeys were made through the station in the first year, and the figure is growing. The adjacent area was subsequently developed with 300 houses and further retail premises. The previously existing park-and-ride site was later moved to the station, which is proving a very worthwhile addition to the Exeter-area rail network.

The lessons learned from this project have prompted the County Council to ensure that all current and future aspirations for rail projects will be taken through a systematic process of concept, feasibility (technical and economic), business plan (to include detailed design and robust cost estimates, with formal legal agreements and approvals from all parties), and finally a construction phase with strong management from both the County Council and the rail industry.

Operating New Stations

Operationally, there are the modest costs of braking and stopping a train, but a critical assumption here is that the extra stop can be accommodated without using additional resources. Each stop costs around 2min, after allowing for the time taken in deceleration and subsequent acceleration as well as that spent stationary. For example, there are now six intermediate stations between Shipley, West Yorkshire, and Skipton. With electric traction and its superior acceleration capabilities, that journey now takes 29/30min. In 1972 when the intermediate stations were limited to two, and with relatively underpowered diesel units, the end-to-end time was 25min, net of a 2min stand at Keighley. Does the existence of the new station in itself cause track capacity problems?

Eventually, the stage is reached when an additional train has to be drafted in to fulfil the timetable, or some other adjustments made elsewhere. New stations are thus not entirely good news; the perceptions of those making a journey which now has additional stops will not be enhanced unless they are also likely users of the new facility.

Longer Distance

A new station scheme need not be aimed at local traffic. Bristol Parkway (1972) is probably among the best examples of a station constructed essentially for long-distance services. Situated where it is, it enables Bristolians to access First Great

Western services running between Paddington and South Wales as well as the Virgin CrossCountry operations.

Other modern stations with an eye primarily perhaps on the long-distance travellers are Stevenage (1973), Birmingham International (1976) and Milton Keynes Central (1982). In each case, these are sufficiently important locations as to build up a substantial clientele.

Another group is that of stations serving airports, represented by Gatwick Airport (1958), Stansted Airport (1991), Manchester Airport (1993), Prestwick International Airport (1994) and two stations at Heathrow (1998). With these, and Luton Airport Parkway (expected soon), the railway is tapping a growing market which is becoming increasingly critical of road congestion. And the one item which is not needed by departing passengers when they arrive at the airport is their car.

Train services for such markets tend to become bespoke as the airport throughput grows; what is now the Gatwick Express operation was the first of these. At least part of the justification was the limited luggage accommodation on the typical Southern outer suburban train, today's Class 421 CIG and Class 423 VEP units. This led to ever more acrimonious conflict between the daily commuter and the air passengers, some jet-lagged but typically with luggage which they would strew over the seats.

There can still be an uneasy operational relationship between dedicated airport services and others. West Anglia Great

Northern's Stansted Express is currently run at 2tph, but this is likely to become 4tph before too long. With only two intermediate calls at Tottenham Hale (all trains) and Bishop's Stortford (alternate trains), this service interacts most uncomfortably with the same operator's local trains trundling along the two-tracked Lea Valley line. As matters stand, there are no passing opportunities at all but nine intermediate stations between Hackney Downs and Broxbourne, a distance of 14 miles. There are a number of possible solutions and these are linked in to Railtrack's West Anglia Route Modernisation project, which is based on the need for signalling renewal. There are both financial and practical advantages in undertaking track and signalling work together as part of a single package wherever possible.

Putting Back the Track

There is much which can be done to restore the capacity of the railway. Quadruple tracks have been reduced to three north of

Bedford on the Midland main line, and to two in the Normanton area. The Glasgow & South Western's Dumfries to Carstairs double-track line is now single, as is much of the Salisbury to Exeter line of the London & South Western. These and similar examples all over the country can be put back much as they were without building new railways. That is not to suggest that it is necessarily an easy or a cheap task. Bridge reconstructions have ignored those tracks which are no longer in place, realignments by slewing tracks have similarly been made possible by there being fewer in place, and the signal engineers have delighted in planting their hardware in the middle of what was once the four foot.

Nevertheless, such restorations are eminently practicable. The difficulties, which are likely to include obtaining legal authority and maybe some land repurchase, are infinitely less than those of building a new railway from scratch. The furore which accompanied the obtaining of powers for the Channel Tunnel Rail Link is of recent memory.

Capacity Where Needed

Restoration of capacity, on the basis of where it can be achieved easily, is not in itself entirely logical. Who really thinks that bringing back double-track between Penistone and Huddersfield would achieve much more than an increase in costs? Such actions need to be driven by a defined need: examine the problem and see what can be done about it.

For this, Railtrack's Network Management Statement (NMS) is the first port of call. This examines 30 or so pinch points which exist either now or are anticipated in the not-too-distant future. Some, like the Leeds station area capacity problem, are in the relatively straightforward category with modest costs. Others are more problematic, such as how to remodel Rugby for the West Coast upgrade. This station has an unenviable location, sandwiched between flying junctions both to the south (to Euston via Weedon and via Northampton) and to the north (for the Trent Valley and for Birmingham). The fast lines pass outside the slow platform lines, which are either side of a typically huge London & North Western island platform with both north and south end bays.

There are also the old favourites such as

Welwyn on the Great Northern. The Hertford North loop is an alternative route to the main line, but doesn't offer comparable journey times. The NMS 1999, in suitably deadpan language, reads as follows:

'The four-track railway reduces to two tracks where it passes over the viaduct at Welwyn and through the adjacent tunnels. The current maximum capacity is 17 trains per hour. Four-tracking with a new viaduct and tunnels will alleviate this bottleneck and enable 30 trains per hour to operate. Current forecasts of demand indicate that this will be required by 2009/10. Feasibility work has been undertaken in the last year.'

Operationally, the argument is difficult to counter, but the mitigation of perceived environmental problems may well turn out to be a major issue. Schemes of this nature are also going to be costly. The present double-track section is a little over two miles in length; of that, 1,492yd are in the two tunnels and the Digswell viaduct is another 500yd. Between Welwyn South Tunnel and the viaduct lies Welwyn North station.

There are also the freight requirements. Lines earmarked for possible additional use and gauge enhancements include Ipswich-Peterborough-Leicester-Nuneaton-Birmingham and the Settle & Carlisle. The latter is in the category of lines which were nearly closed but might now find a new lease of life as an alternative route for freight. EWS is bullish about its requirements; the company is experiencing strong traffic growth in the forestry products, food and drink, consumer goods, automotive components, military and retail sectors. The road competitor also faces increasing congestion, equivalent to a reduction in average speeds of 0.5mph pa for road trunking.

As expressed by Railtrack:

'EWS requires improved access to operate larger, heavier and longer trains. In particular, they want to ensure that sidings for loading and unloading are available where and when they are requested by their customers.'

This refreshingly candid statement leads to a further point. Is the railway really making the best possible use of the capacity which it already has?

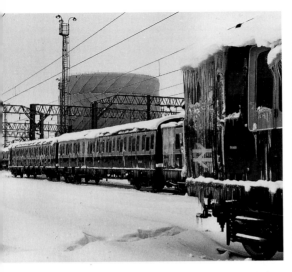

Line Capacity

Suppose passenger operators also saw the way out of the capacity dilemma as the operation of larger, heavier and longer trains. The example of the 26-coach train at King's Cross, with which there would undoubtedly have been problems, has already been discussed. But what alternatives for passenger services are there, of this nature, if line capacity really is going to become much tighter as the years progress?

- Reinvent the double-deck train, not as introduced by Bulleid in 1949 for the Charing Cross-Dartford services, but similar to those found presently in, for instance, Vienna, Zurich and the Netherlands. Bombardier's M12N Eurorail double-deck train for Paris carries over 2,500 passengers in a 10-car train of 224m length. This compares with the 1,744 seats in the 138m of the 10-car Quint-Art sets operated on the Great Eastern steam services out of Liverpool Street, and they were very tight indeed. Different types of double-deck units can be developed for local and long-distance travel. Gauge enhancement work can also benefit the freight operators.
- Make trains up to a maximum of 12 cars or the equivalent. This is the intention for

Thameslink 2000, and has long been the case on many other services. As at many Thameslink stations, platform lengths will need to be extended to suit.
- Produce more uniform service patterns, in terms of station stops and the performance capabilities of the trains used, on any route where there are at present wide variations.
- Review signal spacing to produce an optimum result for the new traffic patterns, with the longer term aim of moving block signalling to enhance track capacity still further.
- Give preferential access conditions to the network for the trains which comply most nearly with the above, but only enforce these in areas where there are defined line-capacity problems.
- Simplify service patterns everywhere to make the whole operation more understandable for staff, as well as passengers. There may be benefits for service punctuality and reliability as well, the performance of which has been less than outstanding in recent times. The first edition of the Great Britain Passenger Timetable in 1975 contained 1,207 pages and was valid for 12 months. The 1999/2000 equivalent has 2,496 pages and is issued twice a year. Are separate tables for Mondays to Fridays, Saturdays and Sundays really necessary?

Such suggestions may border on the verge of heresy for some, but a means will have to be found of matching traffic volumes and infrastructure capabilities in the short, medium and longer terms. Passenger volume growth and the resultant revenue is the key to a profitable franchise and also to a profitable freight operation. It will do wonders for unit costs and for the competitiveness of the railway. More traffic on rail also fits in well with Government views; the 1998 White Paper committed the government as follows:

'To ask the Strategic Rail Authority to develop targets for both the freight and passenger railway to secure the maximum benefit overall from our rail network. In the meantime, we will continue to work towards our objective of moving more freight by rail and towards the targets set by the industry.' (Cm3950, para 3.33).

In the case of EWS, this is to double tonne-km in five years and triple them in 10; Freightliner aims to increase the volume of containers by 50% in five years.

Network Upgrade

This is certainly an option which can and should be pursued, but it has its own drawbacks. The early 1960s saw interminable service dislocations on the West Coast main line, then in course of electrification. Beeching's personal analysis was that the costs of disruption during construction made dieselisation a better option. Electrification meant the loss of traffic and a reduced customer base. In reality, as electrification progressed, trains might proceed diesel-hauled from Preston south to Crewe, change to electric traction as far as Nuneaton, then back to diesel power to Euston. Additionally, Manchester trains were diverted to the Midland route from Central to St Pancras for a matter of years, with the West Midlands traffic served via Birmingham Snow Hill to Paddington.

How can a repeat performance be avoided in future, either on the WCML or perhaps elsewhere? Today's weapons include:

• the selective use of diversionary routes;
• exploiting the flexibility between use of both electric and diesel traction, with the help of Virgin CrossCountry's present fleet

during the fleet replacement programme on the WCML;
• the avoidance of double weaves between fast and slow lines but, above all;
• making sure that train crew rosters and engineering support activities are right at all times.

Conclusions

The railway of the future has plenty of business potential, if only it can be harnessed effectively. There are many parties involved, but nearly all have a common interest in the well-being of railway itself. This book has attempted to examine the system primarily from a practical operational viewpoint, but at the same time taking account of the political and economic environment in which the railway exists.

The railway is a creation of the engineering professions and business interests in Victorian times. Between them, they almost created a design, build, operate and maintain arrangement. The operation of the railway was slowly ceded by the engineers to specialist managers, once equipment reliability and mechanical safety had been established.

In more recent times the railways have been treated as a business, required by the nation for social and economic reasons, with state payments to reflect their public service obligations. The Railways Act 1993 resulted in a completely new industry structure, and the business background was strengthened. Now we have a government concentrating on the problems of pollution and congestion, and how an integrated transport system can help solve them.

Throughout all of this, the railway operator has been largely overlooked. Yet planners can plan, engineers can build the trains and infrastructure, the sales force can drum up the custom, and the City can provide the funds, but operations remain at the heart of the industry. No operators, no railway.

There are huge tasks ahead for the railway operators, who will need to be highly trained and well qualified to take full advantage of the new opportunities which are opening out. It is hoped that this book will contribute a little to their future success, and that they will be able to reinforce this by becoming members of the Institute of Logistics and Transport.

Above:
Merseyside also saw Conway Park station opened in 1998. The station is underground in the sense of being below ground level, if not totally enclosed. This view of unit No 507015 is taken looking towards Birkenhead Park. Full emergency exit arrangements have been included in this new construction. *Author*

Below:
No 47709 belongs to Fragonset Railways, but is seen here on hire to Virgin CrossCountry as it stands at Manchester Piccadilly on 16 March 1999 with the 10.40 Edinburgh-Brighton. Will the relaxation of competition rules entice new operators into the railway market and, if so, what effect is this likely to have? *Author*